a history of physics

THE NEW ILLUSTRATED LIBRARY OF SCIENCE AND INVENTION

CHARLES-ALBERT REICHEN | **a history of physics**

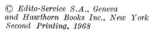

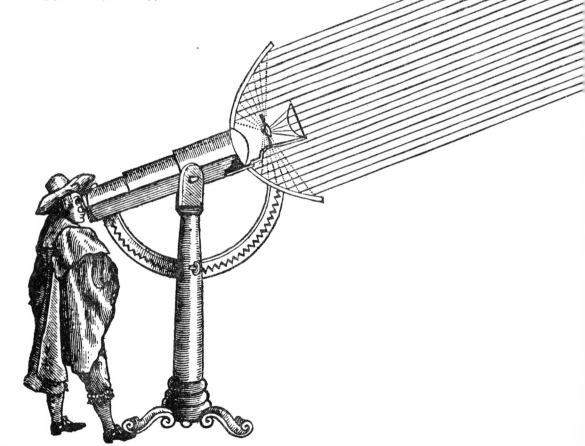

contents

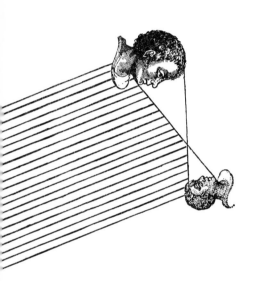

The great French scientist Pierre Duhem once wrote that "only the history of science can protect the physicist from false excesses, either of dogmatism or of scepticism." His warning takes on new meaning today, not only for the physicist but for the layman who wishes to learn something about physics; for during the last hundred years physics—or, if you wish, our understanding of the physical world—has been changing rapidly. It has been growing in depth, complexity, and range. In fact, modern physics in the broadest sense begins to offer, almost despite itself, a radically new view of the origin, structure and possible future of the material world. Both for the layman, who does not command the language of mathematics, and for the physicist, who may not be fully aware of the implications of his own complex studies, a historical view is of the utmost importance in providing some perspective and thus understanding of the remarkable progress of physics. "To describe the history of a physical principle,"wrote Pierre Duhem, "necessarily implies a logical analysis of the problem." In other words, if we retrace the steps which led to the concepts of modern physics, these concepts in themselves will not seem so difficult.

The word "physics" indeed brings to mind two seemingly almost unrelated sciences—as different each from the other as an old-fashioned balance and a huge synchrotron. On the one hand there is classical physics with its familiar levers and gears, its liquids and solids, its forces and pressures, and its clear-cut laws which seem to have defined for all time the logical operations of the natural world. On the other hand there is modern physics (and especially

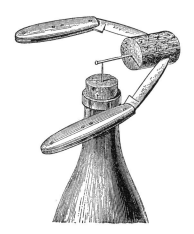

nuclear physics), with its frank inability to describe the all-important electrons as anything more than "clouds of probability," its baffling description of radiation as pertaining both to waves and to particles, and its direful ability to transform matter into energy. The principles of the one built the pyramids and the cathedrals, the principles of the other produced both relativity and the atom bomb.

Yet there is a real relation between the two, and this relation can best be understood in terms of history. Although physics today is not a simple science, a definition of physics which embraces both classical and modern physics can be made quite simple. The physicist, modern or classical, seeks to correlate and explain the operations of the natural world in terms of theory. His tools are observation and experiment; his objective the refinement of theory in an attempt to make it approximate to presumed reality—and, quite incidentally, such practical achievements along the way as radio or the atom bomb. In other words it has been the purpose of the physicist throughout history to understand, as well as to use, the elemental aspects of the world around us—matter, motion, forces, energy. His success has been measured by his ability to interpret the phenomena of the physical world—which, incidentally, accounts for the slow progress of the science until recent years. For along the way the physicist has fallen into many deep pits of "false excesses, either of dogma or of scepticism" and has had to climb out again (having learned a good deal by the experience) to start in another direction.

It is instructive to follow through history the successive approximations by which intelligent minds learn to apprehend reality: fable gives way to metaphysical explanation, which in turn is superseded or confirmed by scientific explanation. And finally, there is the nature of the scientific explanation itself. From the seventeenth until the middle of the nineteenth century a rather simple mechanistic explanation of natural phenomena, derived from experimental contact with the visible, audible and tactile world, dominated physics. It almost provided a complete explanation of observed phenomena, via forces of attraction and repulsion operating across a presumed medium called the aether. The great nineteenth century scientist Helmholtz went so far as to insist that science's "vocation will be ended as soon as the reduction of natural phenomena to simple forces is complete..."

But the dream was not to last. Certain phenomena, especially in light and electricity, which did not fit into the pattern of "simple forces," soon led physicists to penetrate below the sensible surface of observed reality down to the actual structure of matter itself, the atom, the electron, the neutron, positron and meson. What a Pandora's box of uncertainty, of relativity, of wave-like particles, of caged energy was then revealed! It seemed to have no relation to the observable world the physicists used to know. Yet it was still—more truly, if more subtly—the operations of the natural world. The new universe of the infinitely small, as with the new extragalactic universe of the infinitely large, discovered by the astronomers, is something we have to learn to live with. It is becoming an aspect of our general culture. The history of physics, therefore, takes on a new importance.

5   *Fire, lightning, clouds, the composition of the earth
itself—these were little understood when this
conception of the earth's formation appeared in 1714.
Modern physics has not only explained these phenomena
but has given us a startling new picture of our world.*

The tragedy of Hamlet was that thought preceded action. Frequently the order is reversed. Throughout man's history, for example, he has sought to make use of natural forces without reflecting deeply as to their meaning. For this reason, the engineering feats of the ancient world hardly imply a mature understanding of the laws of physics. To take an obvious example, the discovery and use of fire came long before the earliest speculations as to its essential nature.

The working principles of the wedge, the lever, and the winch were known to the earliest men. In the third millennium B.C. the Sumerians used them to erect heavy statues such as that of King Gudea. At about the same time the early Egyptians, although they seem to have known nothing about the wheel, used similar methods to construct the pyramids. Somewhat later the palace of Cnossus was built in Crete. On the Greek mainland the famous "Treasury of Atreus," the tomb of the legendary King of Mycenae and father of Agamemnon was constructed. Many of the mechanical principles used by the ancients are known today by the most primitive tribes, even those with the least aptitude for abstract thought. The Australian aborigine, for instance, cannot count beyond three. Yet he constructs and uses the boomerang which, on missing its mark, returns to its rightful owner, thus following a trajectory that requires an expert in ballistics to explain.

In effect there has been a gap between action and thought. Man the doer, *Homo faber*, seems to have come into the world long before the intellectual, *Homo sapiens*; and perhaps this was because, as the psychologist Delacroix has pointed out, it requires a difficult reorientation

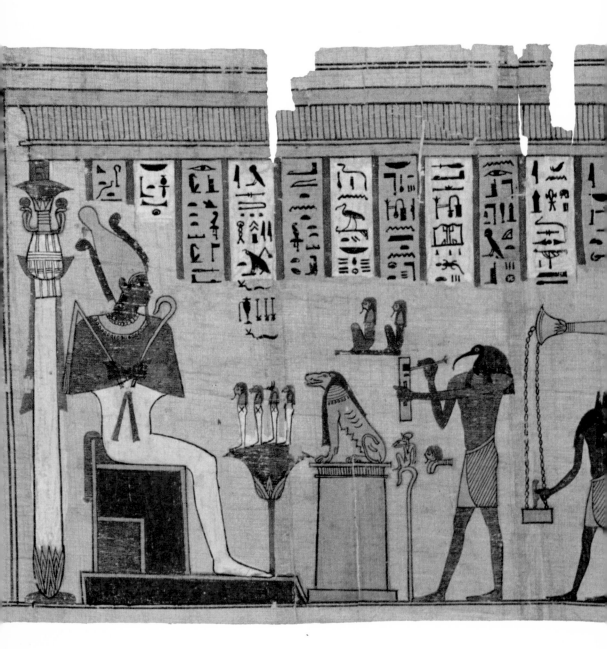

6 *Scales center a depiction of
the judging of the dead—a very
popular theme in Egyptian art.
The peoples of the ancient world
knew little more than the simplest
of mechanical principles and
devices—scales, the wedge, the
lever, the winch. And yet with these
simple tools and lots of manpower
they were able to build the pyramids
of Egypt and Mesopotamia and the
palaces of Crete. In this scene
Osiris, king of the region of the dead
(left, on his throne) judges
the weighing of the soul of the deceased
(right, in white). Ibis-headed
Thot, the light god, records
the proceedings, while dog-headed
Anubis (center) helps with the weighing.
More souls await judgment at the left.*

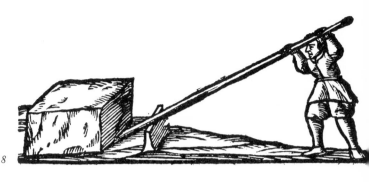

of the mind to pass from technology to science. To start thinking, one must stop acting—a deliberate restraint which is not natural to the human spirit and requires an unusual self-discipline, detachment, and even genius. During the fifth and sixth centuries B.C., for example, only a handful of men in the entire world were capable of this intellectual effort. And so it was that a few Greeks in Ionia began to create physics while at the same time laying the foundations for Western civilization.

This is not to say that their predecessors had no theoretical ideas. A wealth of clay tablets from Mesopotamia indicate that in the age of Sumer and Akkad some of the basic ideas of motion—continuous or discontinuous, accelerated or decelerated—were already well understood. And it was known, at least as a working rule, that velocity was to be calculated by dividing the elapsed distance by the time. To measure distances, the Mesopotamians had excellent and precise instruments calibrated on a sexagesimal scale. For recording time they had water clocks for 12, 24 and 60 hours, as well as sun-dials. If it is confirmed that the water wheel existed in Mesopotamia at the time of King Hammurabi, then we must conclude that the Chaldean engineers were familiar not only with the concept of linear velocity, but knew probably also how to relate it to the angular velocity of the wheel.

But these are pretty simple principles. The Greeks hoped to go much further; in fact they tried to attack the problem of science at the deepest level by establishing a systematic theory of physics logically deduced from certain fundamental assumptions. In the pioneering

theories of Thales, for instance, the basic substance was considered to be water. By condensation it gave rise to solids and by evaporation to air—or gas. Thus the two fundamental forces which underlay Thales' system were those of contraction, and of expansion. The first was called centripetal, the second centrifugal.

Heraclitus, in his philosophy of transformation developed about 500 B.C., stated that all things are in a state of continuous movement, and that nothing is ever lost. More explicitly, Empedocles, about 450 B.C., proposed four fundamental elements: earth, water, air, and fire. These were constantly intermixed and divided among themselves, but in such a way that the total amount of matter always remained constant. In this theory there were again two fundamental forces, colorfully referred to as Love and Hate, but which today we would call the forces of integration and disintegration. According to Empedocles, the second was always a little stronger than the first; thus man lived in a universe in which little by little Hate gained the advantage over Love. We may have reservations about this in the moral sphere, but Empedocles was talking about the material world in which he claimed the forces of dissociation were gradually prevailing over the forces of concentration: a curious foretaste of the modern ideas of an expanding universe and of entropy.

In the theory of Anaxagoras in the fifth century B.C. all forms of energy are reduced to one, called "nous"—not a conscious cosmic intelligence, as one might think, but only "the most fluid of all things and the most pure." It permeates all things and gives them life, which seems to indicate that its nature was

7   *This balancing trick, shown in a drawing from a late 16th century edition of Aristotle's "Mechanics," is tried by children the world over.*
8   *An illustration from a mid-17th century work shows the principle of the lever, used early in history for moving heavy objects.*
9   *Distribution of forces, amusingly shown, from Aristotle's "Mechanics."*

quasi-material. Anaxagoras has been called the father of atomic theory. According to him all matter consists of atoms which have different specific properties, and which he called the seeds of life. These particles, while whirling about in continuous motion, associate together in definite spherical patterns. Anaxagoras also claimed that the air has weight, as well as the moon and the stars, so that if the latter were not rotating at high velocity they would inevitably fall down upon the earth. This anticipation of Newton suggests that Anaxagoras may have carried out experiments on rotational motion.

Democritus (460-370 B.C.) gave Anaxagoras' theory a theoretical unity by postulating that all the atoms were exactly the same, but that the differences in the number of atoms or in their arrangement gave rise to the diverse properties of everyday materials. The atoms, however, had different weights; as the heaviest fell faster, they collided with the lighter atoms and thus created eddies and vortices which formed themselves into new substances. These vortices tended to push the lightest bodies toward the top and if the speed of rotation was sufficiently high they became incandescent.

In the earliest atomic philosophies there was no difficulty in explaining the tendency of the atoms to combine together in different arrangements. It was purely and simply a question of Necessity, a soulless, mechanical necessity corresponding to the modern idea of universal determinism. A good deal later Epicurus (341-270 B.C.) substituted Chance for Necessity, and thus opted for a fundamental indeterminism. It is worthwhile noting that the atom of Democritus and Epicurus had no specific properties; it was neither red nor blue, hot nor cold, wet nor dry, but was characterized only by a specific shape and a specific size. Modern science has completely justified this point of view; and in fact we are bound to admire the daring intellectual initiative of these early atomic theorists. In the words of a modern physicist, "They tried to explain the complications of the visible world by means of a simple, invisible world."

The physical theories of Democritus still recognized the existence of the material world. For example he discusses, much as in the physics of the nineteenth century, the response of massive bodies to the influence of applied forces. Pythagoras, however, took the theory even further into the realm of abstraction. For him numbers, and the mathematical relations between them, made up the only true reality. These mathematical and causal relations between things were more important than the things themselves. As a result the material world was only an illusion, and the forces which appeared there had no existence apart from the numbers which defined their intensity and their direction. One sees here a temptation which some modern theoreticians also have difficulty in avoiding: to treat the atomic particles as no more than an exercise in pure mathematics.

The decline of the Pythagorean School was due to a weakness in its philosophy. While studying the theory of numbers, Philolaus and other disciples of the master noticed to their dismay that certain numbers are irrational. How could one tolerate the existence of numbers which could not be expressed as the ratio of two others? The spark of contradiction had been struck and the mathematical equipment of the

10

14

10-13 *A fresco at Thebes, ancient capital of Egypt, depicts various devices used in the 2nd millennium B.C. At left is a well sweep, the bucket counterweighted with a heavy stone, a simple but effective device which was found in Egypt as early as 1550 B.C. The carrying yoke shown below (11) and scales (12) were of equal antiquity. In wine making (13) the pulp from the trodden grapes was placed in heavy sacks with loops at each end. Poles, inserted in the loops and twisted, squeezed the juice out of the pulp. Olive oil was also made with this type of press.*

11

12

13

Pythagoreans was not adequate to control the resulting conflagration. That is why Plato felt obliged to base his theory on geometry, and in particular on the theory of solids which was very popular at this time. As the simplest figure is the triangle, the basic element was taken as a right-angled triangle, and solids were made up out of combinations of these triangles. The regular polyhedrons played an essential role, the tetrahedron (four faces) corresponding to fire, the octahedron (eight faces) to air, the hexahedron (six faces) to the earth, and the icosahedron (20 faces) to water. Here again appeared the idea of the essential unity of all matter, because by changing the number of constituent triangles one element could be transformed into another. Two tetrahedrons of fire, for example, could be transformed into an octahedron of air and vice-versa; in the same way two and a half octahedrons of air or two octahedrons of air and a tetrahedron of fire could give rise to one icosahedron of water and vice-versa. Thus without making any appeal to atomic theory and using only the idea of pure form, the physics of Plato showed the essential unity of all matter with the implied possibility of transmutation from one form to the other .

Plato also recognized that the weight of a body was due to the effect of a force pushing it downwards; this was his conception of gravity. He also knew something about capillarity and describes several simple experiments he made in this area. In kinematics he distinguished between linear motion and rotary motion, and in discussing the movement of the top he recognized that the axis of rotation tends to be preserved, a fact which became important

later with the invention of the gyroscope. Plato was a strong advocate of experimental research, to which he assigned a very great importance.

Under his pupil Aristotle, however, physics suffered a rather serious setback. This Macedonian philosopher explicitly rejected the atomic point of view and instead of a quantitative theory of matter preferred a rather puerile qualitative approach. He was a poor mathematician and claimed that he could trust nothing but the evidence of his senses. He reduced everything to the simple effect of hot and cold, wet and dry, on raw primary matter, which in itself had no attributes or qualities. This curious primary substance reminds one of the famous "knife without a blade, which has lost its handle" mentioned by Rabelais. He also introduced the idea of the fifth element, or quintessence—often called the aether—which as we shall find later has in many ways formed the basis of a number of theories extending up to the present day. The quintessence was activated by a rotary motion which contrasted with the motion of the light and heavy bodies, the latter normally tending to fall and the former to rise. This was the essential basis of Aristotelian kinematics.

In his mechanics, Aristotle insisted, much as had Pythagoras and Plato, that the action of one body on another could occur through points of mutual contact. His theory of ballistics had some curious aspects. Every trajectory was divided into three parts. The first was one of forced movement, in the second there was mixed movement, and in the third the movement was natural. The trajectory therefore consisted of a rising first part, a middle mixed part which was exactly horizontal, and finally a falling

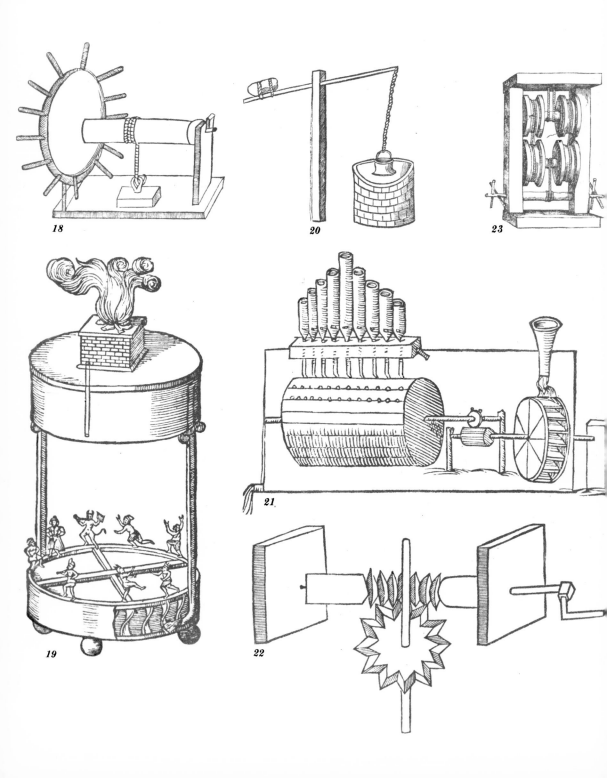

18

20

23

19

21

22

18-28   Mechanical devices of
the ancient world making use of
different principles of physics.
Illustrations taken from
the 1594 edition of Aristotle's
"Mechanics" in Greek (18, 20, 22,
27) include a winch (18), a well
sweep (20) and a pulley (27). A
winch of Archimedes is shown in
a drawing from 1615 (23), and an
Archimedes screw (26) from Jerome
Cardan's "De Subtilitate" (1556).
A water organ (21) is of the type
developed by Hero of Alexandria.
Various illustrations from
Kircher's "Oedipus Aegyptiacus"
showing automats constructed by
Hero (19, 24, 25) include a statue
of Memnon (28) which was animated
by air heated by the sun.

24

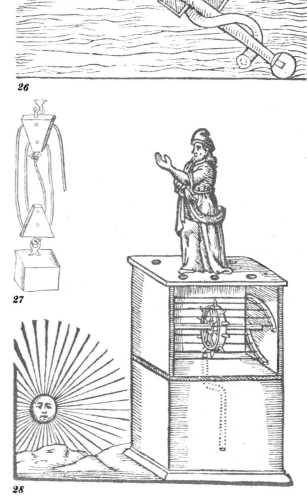

26

27

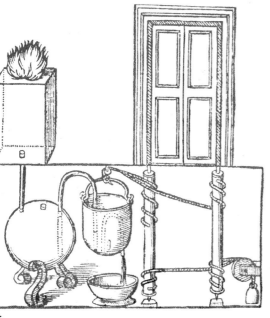

28

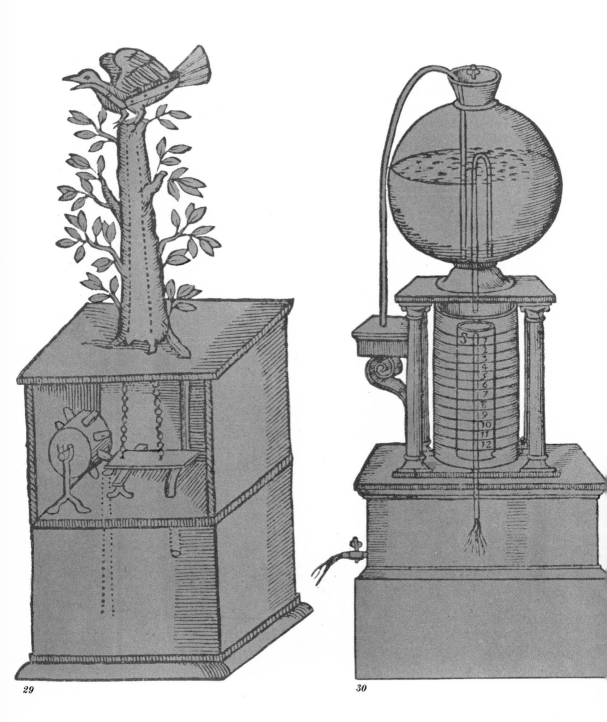

29   30

29-32 *The mechanical ingenuity of the late Greek school of Alexandria is shown in these reconstructions of various automata, taken from Kircher's "Oedipus Aegyptiacus," published in Rome in the 17th century and based upon the writings of Hero of Alexandria. Scholars are divided upon the motive power employed to run these gadgets, although weights, the siphon, and the action of hot air may all have been employed. The flapping bird (29) may have been weight-driven. The water clocks (30 and 32) depended upon a carefully regulated flow of water, while air heated by candles caused milk to flow from the breasts of the goddess (31).*

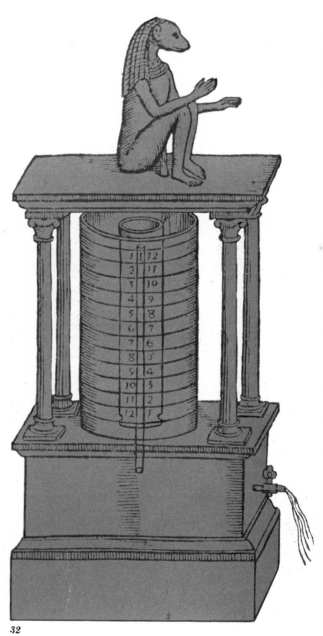

31

32

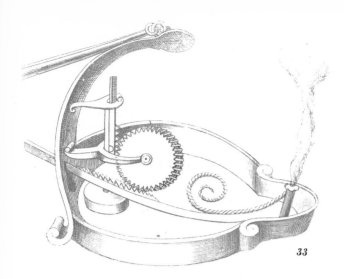

33

part. It was necessary to wait until the year 1537 A.D. for this theory, which was completely contrary to observation, to be definitely refuted by Tartaglia.

The disastrous influence of Aristotelian physics on the progress of science was continued into the Middle Ages, when his ideas were taken up by St. Thomas Aquinas and imposed upon the whole Christian world. It is interesting to note, however, that for 250 years after his death Aristotle's theories were completely ignored by the great physicists of the ancient world: Archimedes, Ctesibios, and Hero of Alexandria. These three geniuses were men of action rather than dreamers, and did their best to separate physics from metaphysics. Everybody has heard of the principle of Archimedes: a body immersed in a liquid is pushed upwards by a buoyant force which is equal to the weight of the liquid displaced. It formed the foundation of the science of hydrostatics, and the applications of the principle are innumerable. Archimedes had really made a very great discovery. Coming out of his bath carrying the crown of gold and the crown of silver which he had used for his experiment, he had good reason, as the story goes, to run all over Syracuse shouting "Eureka!"

Archimedes not only wrote the famous *Treatise on Floating Bodies* but also invented the worm-gear and pinion and other types of gears, and worked out a general theory of the lever. His famous saying is familiar to most: "Give me a fulcrum and a lever long enough and I will move the world!" Archimedes was also a brilliant engineer. When Syracuse was attacked by the Roman fleet he invented a

number of ingenious devices for the defense of the city: the ballista and the catapult for projecting arrows and throwing stones, and enormous cranes which lowered grappling hooks onto the superstructures of the triremes, pulling them against the rocks where they were wrecked. According to legend, the rest of the Roman fleet was set on fire by means of immense parabolic mirrors of burnished bronze which concentrated the rays of the hot Sicilian sun on the enemy galleys! Archimedes' various devices were useful in holding the enemy off and converting the siege into a blockade, but they could not save the city. And in the debacle and massacre that followed Archimedes lost his life at the hands of a Roman soldier.

One of the reasons for the success of this inventive physicist, who solved so many of the problems puzzling the scientists of his day, was that he was also the greatest mathematician of the ancient world. He was responsible, for instance, for a rigorous application of geometry to statics. It was natural for him to use mathematical analysis in formulating the laws of physics. This was also the strength of Galileo, Descartes, and Pascal in a later epoch.

Among the pupils of Archimedes particular mention should be made of Ctesibios whose inventions have been preserved for us in the pages of the Latin writer, Vitruvius. Ctesibios discovered the force pump, which worked by suction, and perfected the hydraulic pipe organ, a keyed instrument which was used not only by the Byzantines but well into the Middle Ages. Towards the end of the eighteenth century a pumping machine attributed to Ctesibios was discovered in the neighborhood of Civitavecchia

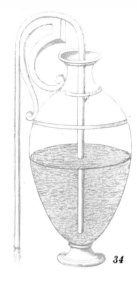

34

in Italy. Around 170 B.C. Philo, who carried on the work of Ctesibios, demonstrated in his essay on pneumatics that the air is a body like any other. His proof was the experiment which has wrongly been called the "balloon of Hero." Philo also laid the foundations of the science of temperature measurement; and in fact his thermometer was a very advanced instrument for the time.

Undoubtedly the greatest experimentalist of antiquity was Hero, who wrote his works about 133 B.C. A very fine mathematician, Hero adopted the division of the circle into 360 degrees, originally brought to the western world by Hipparchus of Bithynia. He was also a renowned teacher and founded at Alexandria a veritable technical school with a special department devoted entirely to research. For Hero, an absolute vacuum could not exist, and he regarded air as a substance of great elasticity which could be compressed or dilated. Thus he was able to give a correct explanation of the phenomenon of suction, accounting for the action of suction apparatus like the pipette, or the cupping-glass. He also used a suction machine for pumping water similar to those of Philo and Ctesibios. Hero is above all famous for his aeolian wheel, or aeolipile, which for the first time made use of the energy of expanding steam and the principle of reaction. An egg-shaped earthenware vessel, equipped with two outlet pipes angled so that they would direct a jet of steam tangentially, was mounted on pivots to turn about a horizontal axis. When the water in the vessel was heated the jets of steam emerging from the two tubes made it rotate at high speed.

In mechanics Hero used a system of gear wheels to solve a problem proposed by Archimedes—that is, to lift a weight of 1,000 kilograms by means of a force of only five kilograms. He also used a parallelogram to make the vector addition of velocities, and studied the mysteries of motion on an inclined plane and the effects of friction. His system for constructing a variable ratio drive by means of a friction disc has been used in our time to make an automobile with semi-automatic transmission. As a result of his study of all these devices Hero was able to formulate the principle: "That which is gained in force is lost in time." In addition, Hero stated the law of inertia in crude form and showed that force is proportional to the mass of the moving body times the speed at which it moves.

Construction engineers owe a debt to Hero for his tables of dimensions used in building arches, and in drilling tunnels and wells. Lovers of detail will be intrigued by the little automata that were constructed by the great physicist for his own amusement; a nightingale which flapped its wings and sang when one pushed open the gates of a temple, the opening of temple doors controlled automatically by the hot air rising from the fire of sacrifices, and so forth.

Aside from these amusements, Hero must be recognized above all as a master in the arts of measurement and as one of the founders of the general science of mechanics. After him there was no further progress in physics for many centuries, and if it had not been for the Arabs it is more than likely that the works of this great scientist would have been lost. Many centuries later they were to serve as an inspiration for Leonardo da Vinci.

35-40 *Figures taken from a late 15th century
manuscript, "La science de la divine proportion"
by Pacciolo. These beautifully rendered geometric
forms, reminiscent of Plato's physics, have been
recently attributed to the pen of Leonardo da Vinci.*

39

40

It might well be maintained that those ages which have been most vigorous in the practical applications of technology have been at the same time periods of relative scientific stagnation, and vice versa. Certainly the Middle Ages, which was renowned for its craftsmanship, for the daring of its architecture, and for the ingenuity of its military invention was more or less sterile in the domain of theoretical research. The thought of the early Middle Ages was in fact entirely dominated by Aristotelian physics—a set of dogmatic assumptions elaborated in detail by the doctors of the church and imposed with all the authority of an accepted faith. The Middle Ages more truly showed its debt to the ancient world in the honor which it paid to Vitruvius, the Roman author who described the inventions of Archimedes and Hero. In fact the works of this prolific compiler formed the basis of the whole of medieval technology; and as there was nothing in Vitruvius' handbook of practical instruction which contradicted the dogmas of their theology, the medieval architects, engineers and craftsmen felt free to exercise their fancy in putting to use these precious recipes handed down to them from the past.

Two major discoveries of the Middle Ages were gunpowder and the compass. The first was briefly mentioned by Roger Bacon in the middle of the thirteenth century; the second, it has been said, was invented in the year 1332 by a humble and otherwise unknown fisherman on the sea coast near Amalfi. Certainly the people of Amalfi knew virtually nothing about the extraordinary property of magnetism which activated their primitive compass—probably adopted by them some time after its discovery

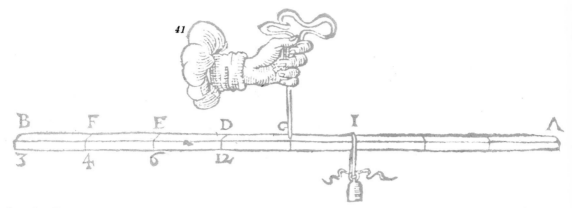

by the Chinese. Nor did the feeble explosions produced by the Franciscan Roger Bacon, from his basic mixture of charcoal, saltpeter, and sulphur produce in him any general conclusions about the nature and pressures of what, after Van Helmont, we now call gases.

The thought of the Middle Ages, then, was essentially practical, utilitarian, and conservative. Nevertheless, the dominant physics of Aristotle was not always accepted without question. In A.D. 517, Johannes Philoponus poked fun at his philosophy, and for the first time put forward a theory of the transmission of momentum from one body to another which was to be accepted for many years. "The energies," he said, "flow from one body to another in such a way that an 'impressed force' is transmitted to the projected body." We have here the theory of action by contact upon which, at a later time, Descartes erected his whole mechanics. About A.D. 1330, contradicting the Aristotelian idea that a body falls by virtue of its being heavy, Heytesbury stated that a freely falling body travels three times as far in the second moment of its fall as in the first. It was discoveries of this sort that led Albert the Great (1193-1280), the teacher of St. Thomas Aquinas, to formulate his declaration "experimentum solum certificat": experiment is the only proof. Little by little, but with many difficulties, the idea of gravity made its way into the world. In A.D. 1230, for example, Jordanus Nemorarius issued his tract entitled *Gravitas secundum situs* (Gravity in relation to place).

The all-too-rare theoretician of the Middle Ages was primarily concerned with the study of mechanics and statics. However Nicolas de Cusa (1401-1464) studied hydrostatics and invented the first bathometer based on the reduction in the weight of a submerged body, as well as the first hygrometer which measured on a scale the moisture absorbed by a bundle of sheep's wool. Renaissance physics made a more vigorous beginning with the works of Leonardo da Vinci (1452-1519), who made a close study of Hero, taking over from him a number of mechanical and theoretical ideas, including the theory of levers. Leonardo borrowed the thermometer from Philo and the worm gear and pinion from Archimedes. The Greeks had been greatly preoccupied with the study of the coefficient of friction. Leonardo took it up again, and showed that the frictional force on a many-sided body was the same "whichever way up the body was placed provided only that the supporting surface was flat." He also invented ball bearings and roller bearings, and gave a logical explanation of motion on an inclined plane, categorically eliminating any idea of perpetual motion. This led to his famous theorem: "All bodies exert their weight in the direction of their movement." As the result of endless experiments with balls rolling down ramps of marble or wood he discovered that the velocity increases in uniform arithmetic progression. Extrapolating boldly from this, he concluded that for a freely falling body the speed increased in equal steps for equal intervals of time (constant acceleration), thus anticipating the famous formula of Galileo: $V = gt$.

In hydrostatics, experimenting with communicating vessels, Leonardo extended the existing rule to the case of two different liquids

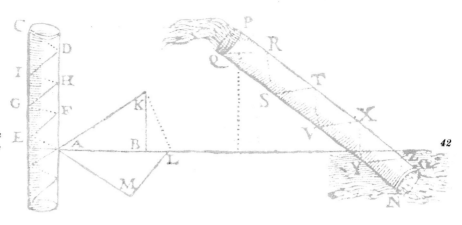

42

and showed that the equilibrium heights were inversely proportional to their specific gravities. But if we exclude from consideration his flying machines, Leonardo's greatest glory was undoubtedly his work on the propagation of waves, either those produced by the wind or by a falling stone. Perceiving that two wave trains can interfere with each other, he concluded that the interference of primary and reflected waves gives rise to the phenomenon of undertow. This was almost certainly the first systematic study ever to be carried out on wave motion.

Although Copernicus was primarily an astronomer, his ideas were expressed in terms of physics. Thus the planets moving around the sun were merely projectiles obeying the laws of ballistics, a coarsely sacrilegious idea which was vigorously attacked by the Thomists, who had no intention of allowing the guiding intelligences of Aristotle or the little angels of St. Thomas to be ejected from their crystal spheres. Galileo, who was as much a physicist as an astronomer, deliberately braved the furies of the Inquisition in order to refute Aristotle who, for instance, had maintained that heavier bodies fall faster than light bodies. According to legend he dropped a leaden ball and a wooden ball of the same size simultaneously from the top of the leaning tower of Pisa, and was able to show that they reached the ground at the same time. This simple experiment brought Galileo both fame and the hatred of the Inquisition.

The experiments with falling bodies undertaken by so many scientists during the sixteenth and seventeenth centuries were designed primarily to demonstrate the rotation of the earth. Neither Galileo nor his successors succeeded in this task, though Galileo was able to formulate the rule that the height from which a body was released was proportional to the square of the time of fall ($h = \frac{1}{2} gt^2$). Not until Foucault in 1851 was the rotation of the earth convincingly demonstrated.

Whether or not Galileo ever considered that there is a relation between the law of falling bodies and the uniform motion of the pendulum must remain an open question. In any case, it has been said that when he was scarcely 19 he turned his attention to one of the swinging chandeliers in the cathedral of Pisa, and by measuring its swing against his own pulse he found that it remained constant. He later formulated the rule that the length of a pendulum is proportional to the square of its period.

This story of the chandelier vividly illustrates Galileo's extraordinary powers of observation. One day a master plumber of Florence found that it was impossible to raise water higher than 18 spans (about 10 meters) by capillary attraction, no matter how large the pumps. Galileo, sceptical, came to see for himself, and after verifying the fact, concluded for want of a better explanation "that nature abhors a vacuum much less than Aristotle had supposed." Galileo was here on the verge of discovering the effects of atmospheric pressure, which were to be explained later by Torricelli and Pascal.

The astronomical discoveries of Galileo have no place in this book, although his detailed description of the telescope named after him, written in 1610, illustrates his great interest in optics. It was the inspired charlatan, J. B. Porta, who first publicized the idea of the refracting telescope in 1590 in his book, *Natural Magic*,

43 *Method for refloating
sunken ships, used in the late
Middle Ages, from
Jerome Cardan's "De
Subtilitate," published
in Paris in 1556.
44 Machine for raising
water, from a 16th century
illustration. As the man
turns the handle of
the winch, the full bucket
(right) is raised while
at the same time the empty
one is lowered. The whole
platform is then swivelled,
reversing the position
of the two buckets.*

43

after which a Dutchman, Zacharias Jansen, constructed the first spyglass between 1590 and 1609. It is interesting to note that while Kepler, once he had the telescope, tried in his *Dioptrics* (1611) to calculate the angle of refraction of rays of light, Galileo, who introduced the telescope to astronomy, never thought of it as anything more than as a means for exploring the heavens.

The same empirical approach was exhibited at about the same time in the development of the first microscopes, which were ungainly instruments about the same size as the telescopes. "With this long cannon," wrote Jean du Pont de Tarde after a visit he paid to Galileo in 1615, "you can see flies which appear to be as big as sheep. They are covered with hairs and have sharp, pointed nails." Not until 1666 did the microscope take the shape we are familiar with today.

Experimental observation is at the very root of the scientific method. When followed by imaginative inductive reasoning it leads to the formulation of the great scientific laws. Experiment, however, cannot be carried out at random and a systematic method is therefore absolutely necessary in the prosecution of research. Such a code, valid for physics as well as for the other scientific disciplines, was formulated by Francis Bacon (1561-1626) of England. As unscrupulous in his politics as he was meticulous in his logic, Bacon was not simply content to disprove the arbitrary assertions of Aristotle and St. Thomas, but launched a direct attack, in his *Novum Organum* and other works, on the whole traditional methodology of the schoolmen. Instead of deriving facts from general principles, he proposed to start from the facts and arrive at the general laws. With masterly

clarity, he isolated the sources of error which could divert the scientist from his goal, and his tables of absence, presence and degree show how to make a clear scientific inventory of the phenomena under observation.

If to become a good physicist one only needs to be a good observer, then physics would indeed be a dull subject. Bacon's contemporaries and successors, without losing sight of the lessons of their experiments, used all their ingenuity to apply abstract reason to the analysis of physical phenomena. It was Galileo who said, "No one will be able to read the great book of the universe if he does not understand its language, which is that of mathematics." René Descartes carried this out, making brilliant use of the science of numbers and creating geometrical optics. His general theory of physics dominated the seventeenth century. It consisted of three main propositions: 1) Everything remains in the state in which it is as long as nothing happens to change it; 2) The total amount of momentum in the world is always conserved; 3) Every moving body tends to continue its motion in a straight line. A physics built strictly upon the ideas of motion, and of extension, or space, had no place in it for the atom, which according to Descartes was "a pure figment of the imagination"; nor for the vacuum, since matter was only another aspect of space. Since there was no vacuum, motion in one body had to be followed immediately by motion in another, one bit of matter taking the place of another. Obviously, with such complicated motions, bodies would always be deflected from the straight line and in fact would follow a curve which eventually looped back on itself.

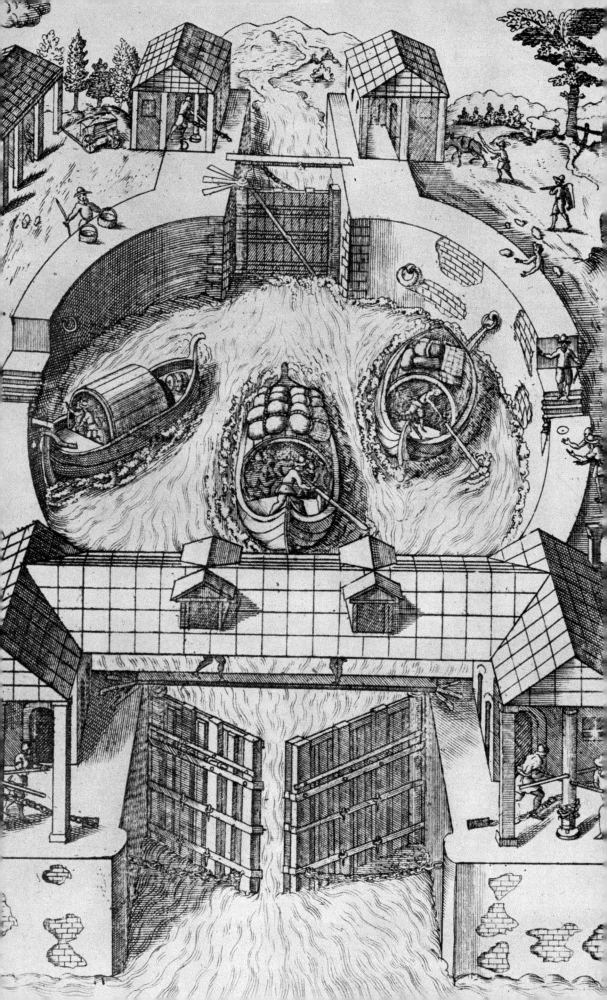

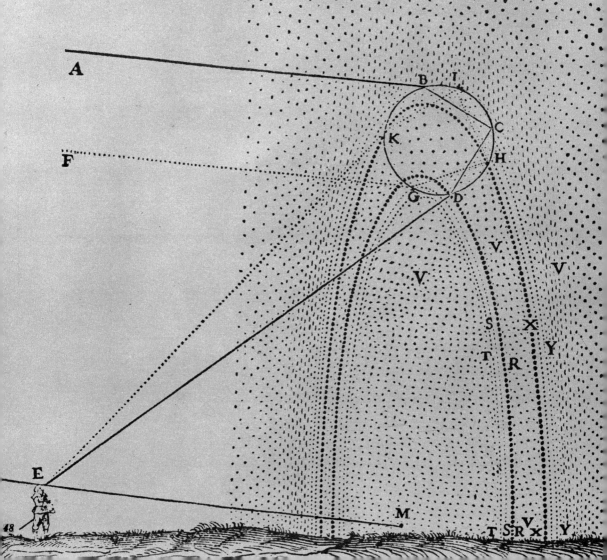

47 This diagram from Descartes'
"Principia Philosophiae,"
in a 1664 edition, illustrates his
famous "theory of vortices." The
mechanistic physics of Descartes,
based upon ideas of motion,
dominated the 17th
century. For Descartes, neither
the atom, nor the vacuum existed,
and motion at a distance was
unthinkable. Matter and space
were one, and matter in motion,
constantly deflected from the
straight line, tended to move in
circles or eddies, or vortices.
48 A diagram from Descartes'
"Dioptrics" showing the optical
decomposition of the rainbow,
one aspect of his fruitful
studies of light.

48

49

Thus arose Descartes' "theory of vortices" in which, apart from the absolutely straight trajectory of light rays, all real movements in the universe are in the form of waves, eddies, or pure circular motion.

With such a mechanistic view of the universe it is understandable why action at a distance had no place in Cartesian mechanics. To explain the effect of a magnet upon iron filings, Descartes had to resort to the idea of a multitude of minute, invisible screws which, upon turning, pulled the iron particles toward the magnet! This was nothing but the old idea of the "vis impressa" or action by contact. In his refraction studies Descartes was far more successful. His rules for calculating relations between the object, the focal length of the lens, and the images, real or virtual, introduced precision and rigor into the subject. It is unfortunate, however, that in his *Dioptrics* of 1637 Descartes was again misled by the mechanistic emphasis of his philosophy to make a false analogy between a ray of light being reflected from a refracting surface and a ball bouncing off a smooth, hard surface. Carrying out the analogy in mechanical terms to explain refraction from a denser to a rarer medium and vice versa, Descartes was led to suppose that the velocity of light was greater in water than in air, a mistake which illustrates the danger of always trying to find an explanation, no matter how artificial it may be.

Though the physics of Descartes maintained its great popularity until the end of the seventeenth century, in his insistence upon rationalism the master had fallen into the same error for which he had so much criticized Aristotle—deducing physical theory from metaphysical principles instead of the other way around. "The essential preliminary to all reasoning," said Pascal in criticizing such exaggerated flights of rationalism, "is to realize that there are an infinite number of things which one cannot understand."

Experiment began to come into fashion again after the second quarter of the seventeenth century. The great men of the period—Torricelli, Pascal, Boyle, and Mariotte—were all enthusiastic experimentalists, applying their talents particularly to the study of gases and the pressure of the atmosphere, a subject which, aside from certain brilliant intuitions of Bacon and Galileo, had scarcely been touched upon. Following Aristotle, it was still thought that nature abhorred a vacuum; indeed, according to Pascal's sardonic comment, "nature would rather disappear altogether than leave the slightest bit of space empty."

Torricelli's famous vacuum experiment was carried out in 1643. Recalling the amazing experience of the master plumber of Florence, he decided to replace the water in the pipes by mercury, guessing that the denser liquid would not rise as high and the apparatus necessary for studying the phenomenon would therefore be much simpler. Actually he used a glass tube four feet high, one end of which was open and the other hermetically sealed. "Having filled the tube with quicksilver and covered the opening with my thumb, I turned the tube upside down and plunged the open end two or three centimeters below the surface of the mercury in the reservoir." On removing his thumb he noticed that the level of the liquid in the tube had fallen, leaving above it an apparently empty space.

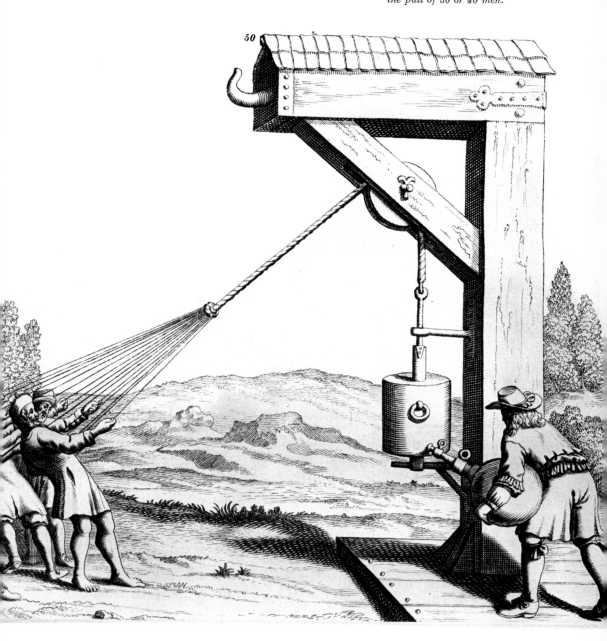

49 Drawing illustrating Galileo's theory of the cantilever (any projecting beam supported only at one end), a principle that has been of extreme importance in engineering and architecture.

50 The force of atmospheric pressure is demonstrated by Otto von Guericke in one of a number of pneumatic experiments—including that of the famous "Magdeburg spheres"—carried out in 1654. The man at right evacuates a cylinder equipped with an airtight piston (at end of rope). Air pressure pushes the piston down into the cylinder despite the pull of 30 or 40 men.

50

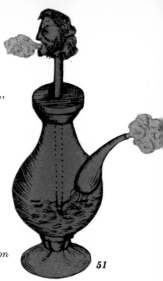

51-52 *Apparatus for various experiments in hydraulics and atmospheric pressure, as illustrated in Francesco Lana's "Magisterum Naturae" of 1686. Lana, a Jesuit priest, was famous in his day for his plans for an airship which was to have been raised by evacuated copper globes. Published in 1670 his plan was widely discussed. It was a clever (though impractical) application of the vacuum.* **51**

More remarkable still, the height of the mercury column remained constant, at about 76 centimeters. It was the striking invariability of this height that had to be explained.

It is hard to imagine today the lively interest that was aroused by this experiment. Roberval thought that the mercury in the tube must be attracted by and held down by that in the reservoir. Pascal, on the other hand, maintained that the mystery could be explained by a certain atmospheric pressure that balanced the weight of the column of quicksilver. If he was right, the height of the mercury column would naturally decrease with altitude. This suggested a crucial experiment; Pascal therefore asked his brother-in-law, M. Périer, to carry the apparatus up the Puy-de-Dôme and make the necessary measurements at the top. The experiment took place on September 19, 1648, and fully bore out Pascal's idea. Although the Jesuit, Father Noël, continued to argue that the observed facts were to be explained by a "light airiness" of the mercury and by "a subtle air which penetrated through the tiny pores in the glass," it had definitely been established that nature had no more horror of a vacuum than of anything else.

The disciples of St. Thomas were in full retreat, and it was only a matter of time before all scientists acknowledged the existence of the vacuum. The "Accademia del Cimento," founded at Florence in 1657, proposed a study of the vacuum. A German, Otto von Guericke, experimenting with the classical syringe, ended up by constructing the first pneumatic machine in 1650. The vacuum he created was not as good as that obtained by the falling mercury in a barometric tube, but the machine was easier to use and more economical. Robert Boyle, Mariotte, Denis Papin, Hooke, and Hawkesbee, immediately grasping the importance of the discovery, set out to improve the apparatus and to carry out new experiments. They found, for instance, that animals die in a vacuum and combustion is impossible, but the magnetic needle continues implacably to point towards the north. It was Otto von Guericke, however, with his famous "Magdeburg hemispheres" who carried out the most spectacular experiment of all—and that in the presence of the Emperor Ferdinand III and his court. A vacuum was created inside a hollow metal sphere, made of two hemispheres sealed tight with a mixture of grease, wax, and turpentine. Teams of horses, eight on a side, could not separate the hemispheres—until air was allowed to enter, when they easily fell apart.

Less sensational but even more important was the discovery by Robert Boyle (as well as by the French priest Mariotte) of the law which bears their names and which for the first time established a definite relation of inverse proportionality between the volume of a gas and its pressure. This could very well be called the first triumph of mathematical physics, for the discovery of this law exhibited that essential collaboration between abstract reason and the experimental method which was to mark the future of physics. Man's intelligence had begun to penetrate the almost incomprehensible diversity of nature; and the most astonishing aspect of this crucial advance was the simplicity of the means employed. All that was required to discover a universal truth was a crude glass tube and a reservoir of mercury.

52

53   *Children gaze spell-bound at magic lantern projections
in this illustration from an 18th century book. Developed in
the 17th century by a German scientist, Kircher, the
magic lantern is the oldest and simplest of projectors.
Above, a cross-section shows the position of the lens.*

"I do not make hypotheses," said Sir Isaac Newton, whose striking personality was to dominate the whole period now under discussion. Not to make hypotheses, or at least not to make hypotheses which cannot be verified, was the main preoccupation of the physicists of the post-Cartesian era. As a result, the final quarter of the seventeenth century and the whole of the century which followed was dominated by a very definite philosophical point of view, and one that can be regarded as typically English: that is, empiricism. The followers of Locke and Hume were inclined to discard anything that appeared to be a purely mental construct. Experience was for them the source of all knowledge, and as experience is based on facts, adventurous flights of the imagination were frowned upon. Fortunately this obsession with the real world did not put a stop to mathematical speculation nor to the brilliant extrapolations of the scientists. Newton himself was responsible for one of the most elegant hypotheses ever put forward, that of universal gravitation; but it was suggested to him, as the story goes, by the very prosaic falling of an apple in his orchard.

Assuming that gravity acts upon the heavenly bodies as well as upon those on earth, the task Newton set for himself was to discover by calculation a valid relation between Kepler's laws of planetary motion and the Galilean laws of falling bodies. He knew for instance that the square of the revolution period of a planet is proportional to the cube of its distance from the sun; also that the force of gravity, acting for example on the falling apple, is inversely proportional to the square of its distance from the

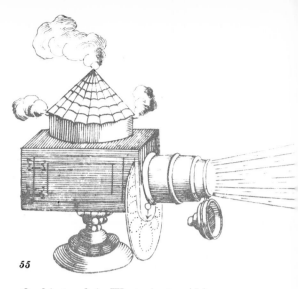

center of the earth. Therefore the apple and the moon must be falling under the action of the same force; and so, starting from a very ordinary fact, Newton postulated the existence of a universal attractive force hitherto quite unsuspected. Naturally, this new interpretation of an age-old phenomenon was to be of tremendous value to astronomy; in physics, however, it introduced an unthinkable, a scandalous concept, that of action at a distance! Newton himself admitted that he could offer no explanation of this extraordinary phenomenon. As he had said, "I do not make hypotheses." Thus by staying within the limits of his experimental experience he remained faithful to the spirit of his day.

Newton was born in 1642 and died in 1727, in his eighty-fifth year. He was brought up on his father's farm at Woolsthorpe, near Grantham in Lincolnshire. Delicate as a child, he became very adept at constructing mechanical toys and gadgets and one of his sundials still survives at Grantham Grammar School. As an undergraduate in Trinity College, Cambridge after 1661 Newton led a quiet life. Not until 1665, when he had taken his B.A. degree and was living at home because of the plague did his genius burst forth in his first series of discoveries. Eventually he became a Fellow of Trinity College, and Lucasian Professor of Mathematics, and after 1703 was annually elected President of the Royal Society until his death. He also served as Warden and Master of the Mint and received a knighthood in 1705. Seldom has a genius received such recognition by his countrymen in his lifetime as Newton, although his ideas were slow to penetrate abroad.

On his tomb in Westminster Abbey one may read, "His life brings honor to the whole human race." Never has such a eulogy been better deserved. Discovering the mathematical technique of the differential calculus in 1666, Newton immediately began planning to apply it to the laws of planetary motion. In 1672 he presented to the Royal Society his paper called *New Theory about Light and Colors*. Everyone today knows something about the prism and how it decomposes white light into separate bands of color running from red to violet. This phenomenon however was a considerable surprise to the contemporaries of Newton who believed, following Aristotle, that the color of a body was inherent in the body itself. Newton was able to demonstrate that color depends solely upon the nature of the light thrown on a body. The different radiations in a spectrum are absorbed in varying degrees so that only certain colors are reflected. "The variety of colors," said Newton, "comes from the fact that light itself is made up of rays of different colors." Needless to say this theory provoked vigorous controversy, but in the end it proved impossible to refute Newton's findings. "If you wish to question nature by means of experiment and observation," Fontenelle said later, "follow the method of Newton, who was not only skillful but insistent." Although Newton was a mathematical genius, it is obvious that he was more honored in his lifetime for his achievements in experimental science.

Among these was his invention of the reflecting, or mirror telescope in 1668, as a result of his study of the chromatic or color defects of the ordinary, or refracting telescope. Although

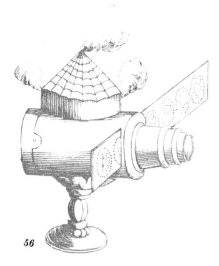

56

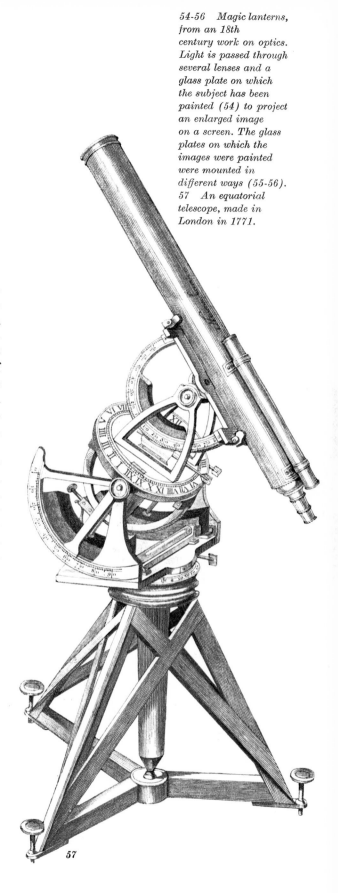

54-56 Magic lanterns, from an 18th century work on optics. Light is passed through several lenses and a glass plate on which the subject has been painted (54) to project an enlarged image on a screen. The glass plates on which the images were painted were mounted in different ways (55-56). 57 An equatorial telescope, made in London in 1771.

Newton despaired of eliminating these chromatic defects and turned to the reflecting telescope to overcome them, Chester Hall and John Dolland did succeed during the eighteenth century in inventing an achromatic lens. In 1675 Newton published his corpuscular theory of light, which anticipated the discovery of the "photon," or packet of light, by Planck and Einstein. Unfortunately, certain phenomena such as diffraction did not fit in at all well with the theory, and Newton was much criticized, especially by Hooke, who pitilessly exposed the contradictions in the corpuscular theory. In 1690 Christian Huygens in his turn published his *Essay on the Nature of Light* in which he suggested that, just as sound propagates through the air in the form of longitudinal waves, so light was a wave motion that travelled through the aether, a special medium which permeated all bodies. Huygens' essay proved to be very influential.

Although the theory was a return to Aristotle's concept of the "quintessence," it did explain a large number of optical phenomena and it was for this reason that throughout the nineteenth century light was universally considered as waves in the aether. The theory explained, for instance, the double refraction of Iceland Spar, and that shadows are never ideally sharp at the edges. In 1801 Thomas Young, professor at London's Royal Institution, seemed to have given the "coup de grâce" to the corpuscular theory by his discovery of interference. Thereafter physicists regarded Newton's idea as hopelessly outmoded until Einstein in 1905 showed that there was some sense in the concept after all.

57

41

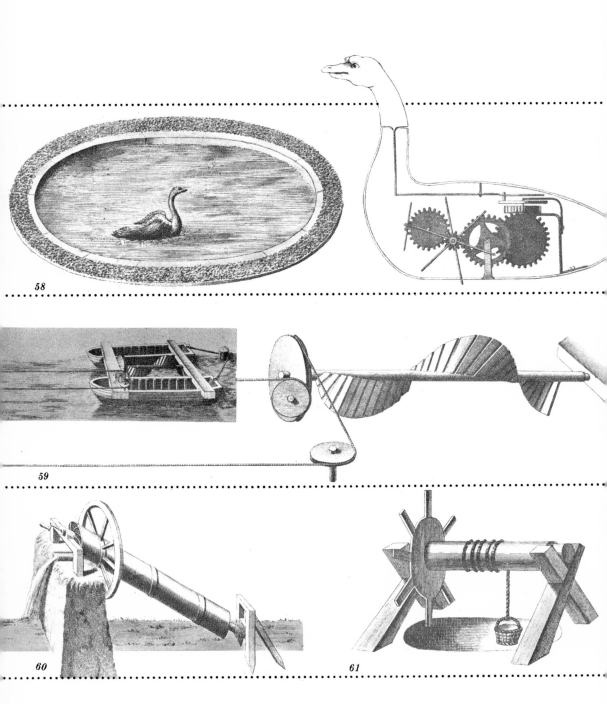

58

59

60

61

62

63

64

65

Newton's master work, this time in pure mechanics, was of course his *Mathematical Principles of Natural Philosophy* or "*Principia*," in three volumes, the first completed in 1685, the rest in 1686 and the whole, after some delays, published in July of 1687. With some lack of confidence in his own ideas, Newton almost gave up the work, but Edmund Halley, the astronomer, took it upon himself (the Royal Society being out of funds at the time) to act as financial guarantor of the publication. Few books have been as influential as the *Principia*, a remarkable synthesis which attempted to show in detail how the principle of gravitation as well as the laws of motion applied not only to the smallest bits of matter on earth but also to the largest of heavenly bodies, as well as to such irregular phenomena as the tides and comets. It is in the *Principia* also that we find for the first time Newton's famous law of the equivalence of action and reaction, a fundamental principle which is at the basis of modern space rocketry. As an interesting sidelight, it was Newton who first had the idea of a jet-propelled car, equipped with a powerful steam nozzle to drive it forward. But of course this was a mere bagatelle for a mind such as his.

Christian Huygens, long Newton's adversary, was not one to neglect the science of general mechanics. His contributions to dynamics were fundamental. He invented the pendulum to control the action of clocks, as well as the balance wheel and spring used in modern watches. As an astronomer he was able to discover the rings and the first satellite of Saturn in 1655. One of his major contributions was the *Horlogium Oscillatorium*, in which he pointed out that when a system of several bodies is allowed to move under the influence of gravity, the center of mass cannot rise higher than it was at the beginning. Also, that a system of three bodies can be moved about without using up any energy, as long as they are confined to the horizontal plane through the center of mass of the system. These discoveries may appear somewhat abstract but are actually fundamental to the science of general mechanics and were to inspire Euler's essay *On the Theory of Solid Bodies*, published in 1765.

The early years of the eighteenth century also saw great progress in the art of temperature measurement. In 1701 Newton constructed the first really practical thermometer. Somewhat earlier the scientists of the famous Florentine Academy had made an alcohol thermometer which they used to observe the freezing point of water. But the graduations on the Florentine thermometer were absolutely arbitrary: once the tube of a thermometer had been sealed they lowered it into a deep cellar where the level of the liquid column was then marked as the zero point. Newton's procedure represented a definite advance. The tube and bulb of the thermometer were first evacuated and then half filled with oil. To calibrate his apparatus, Newton chose as lower fixed point the temperature of melting ice. The upper fixed point was marked 34 degrees, a value he assigned to the temperature of the human body, chosen because it was remarkably constant. Above 34 degrees the graduation was continued but inevitably in a very imprecise way, because at this epoch it was still not realized that water boils at a fixed temperature. This discovery was made in 1702 by the Parisian

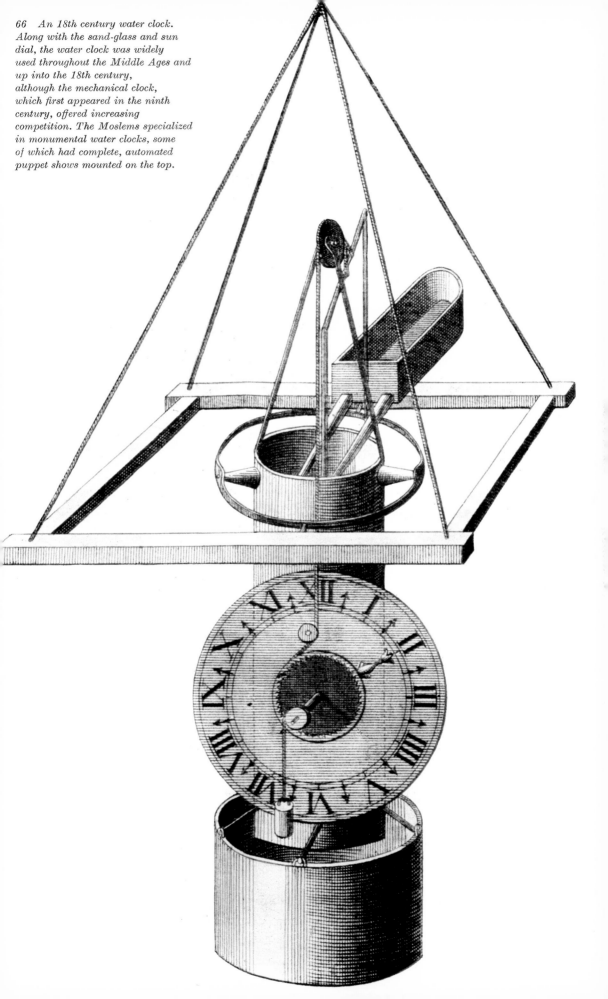

*66 An 18th century water clock.
Along with the sand-glass and sun
dial, the water clock was widely
used throughout the Middle Ages and
up into the 18th century,
although the mechanical clock,
which first appeared in the ninth
century, offered increasing
competition. The Moslems specialized
in monumental water clocks, some
of which had complete, automated
puppet shows mounted on the top.*

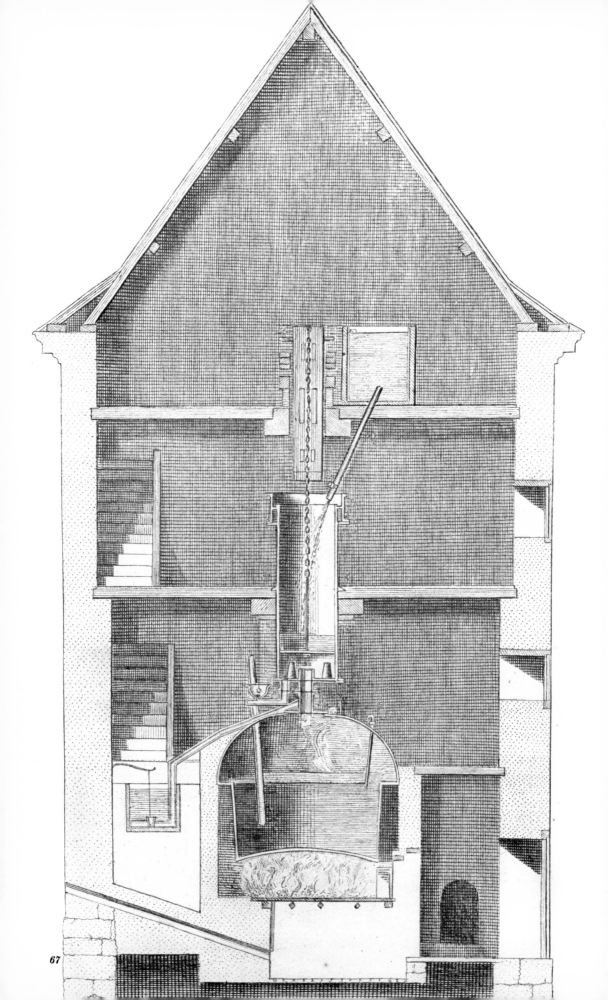

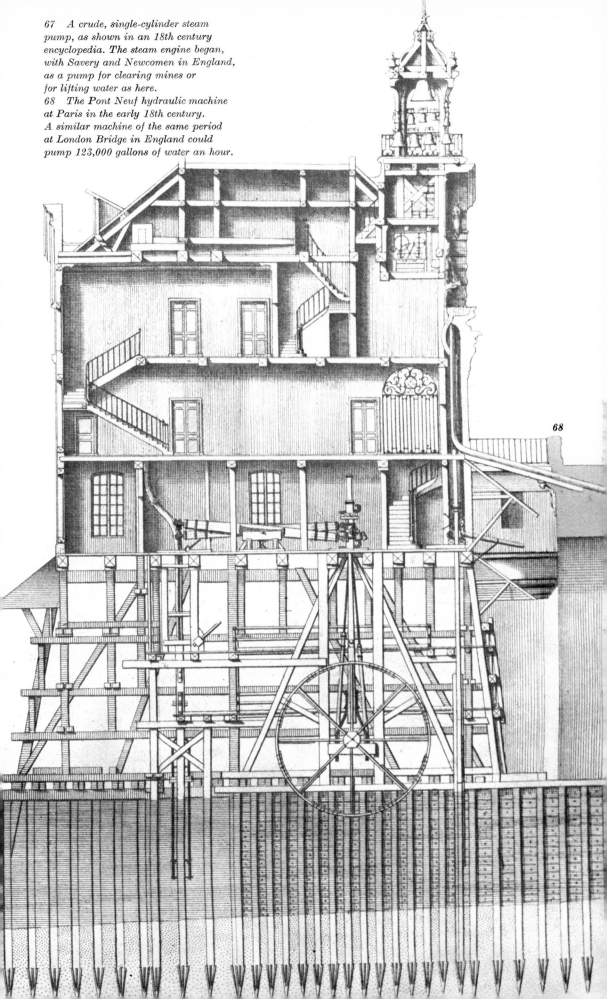

67 A crude, single-cylinder steam
pump, as shown in an 18th century
encyclopedia. The steam engine began,
with Savery and Newcomen in England,
as a pump for clearing mines or
for lifting water as here.
68 The Pont Neuf hydraulic machine
at Paris in the early 18th century.
A similar machine of the same period
at London Bridge in England could
pump 123,000 gallons of water an hour.

68

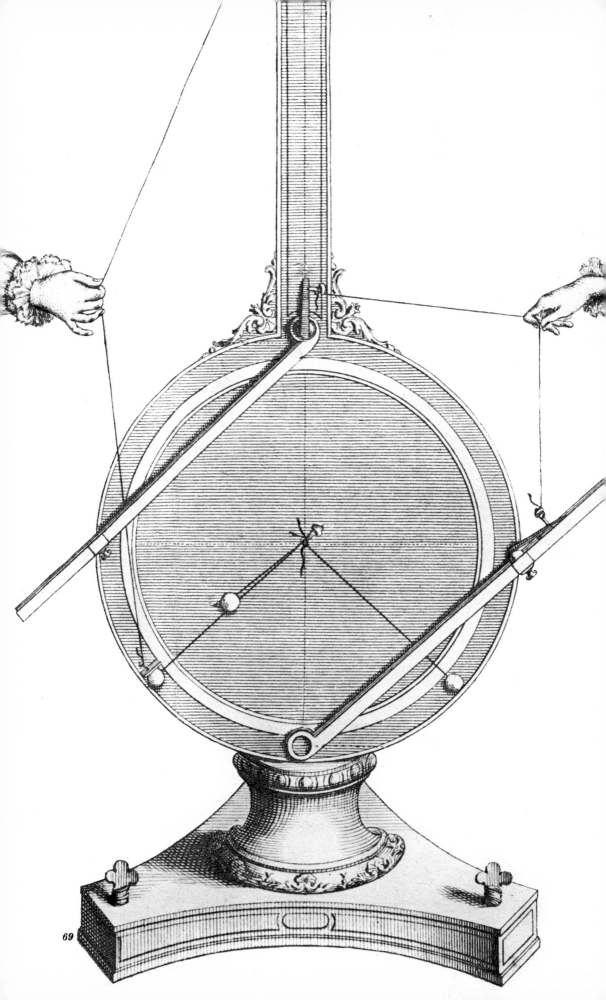

69

69-71 *Experimental apparatus of the Abbé Nollet, from the 1749 edition of his "Leçons de physique expérimentale." A fine physicist himself, the Abbé was an indefatigable popularizer of the new sciences of the day, remembered especially for his well-publicized experiments in static electricity.*
His "Leçons" was an outgrowth of a series of popular lectures he gave for a number of years. Shown here are machines of his own invention with which he demonstrated the laws of falling bodies (69), the spiral and the ellipse (70), the operation of friction (71) and other principles and concepts of physics.

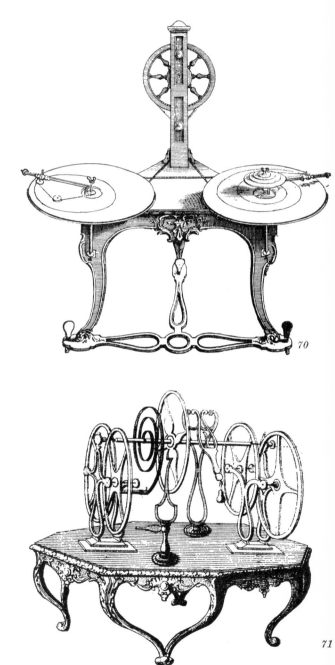

scientist Guillaume Amontons, who used the boiling point of water as the upper fixed point and constructed a rather unwieldy and inconvenient air thermometer before deciding finally on a device based on mercury. About 1714 Daniel-Gabriel Fahrenheit, comparing the boiling points of a number of liquids, introduced the familiar scale still known by his name. Thereafter the importance of these fixed points was recognized, but the precision with which they were determined was still not very exact.

In 1730 Réaumur devised a new thermometer using alcohol and this time the graduations were set up with complete scientific rigor. But here again the instrument was extremely clumsy and it was necessary to wait until the year 1742 for the Swedish physicist A. Celsius to devise a mercury thermometer which was calibrated with zero corresponding to boiling water and 100° to melting ice. By inverting these two calibration figures one arrives at the modern centigrade scale. Celsius was also the first to make a serious study of the influence of atmospheric pressure on the boiling point of liquids, a phenomenon which every motorist crossing a high mountain pass will have noticed, perhaps to his dismay.

The measuring of temperature inevitably suggests thermodynamics, although it was many years before Sadi Carnot, with his *Reflections on the Motive Power of Fire*, was to lay the theoretical foundations of the science. As usual in the history of science, steam power was in use long before the theory it illustrates was defined. It seems that Denis Papin, a little-known scientist who was a friend of Huygens and of Boyle, was the first to propose that a vacuum might be

72

73

72-75 *Compound microscopes,*
17th and 18th centuries.
The compound microscope, in which several
convergent lenses are combined, was
invented by Dutch spectacle-maker
Zacharias Jansen in the 16th century.
Magnifying glasses had been known in
ancient times, and the simple microscope,
made up of a short tube with a lens at one
end and plate glass at the other,
continued to be used by some scientists
through the 17th century, since
the first compound microscopes were
often unsatisfactory. One of the best
known of early compound microscopes
was that of Robert Hooke (73), who
described his adventures with the
microscope in his "Micrographia" of
1665. Also shown here are three
18th century microscopes: Marshall's,
of 1715 (75), a Dutch instrument with
three lenses, called a reflecting microscope
(74), and an Italian microscope (72),
late 18th century.

74

75

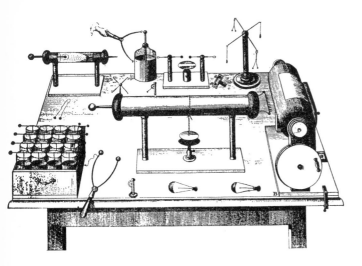

produced under a piston by condensing steam. Papin, a modest and attractive man, led a tragic life. Forced into exile in Marburg after the repeal of the Edict of Nantes in 1685, he died there in extreme poverty, complaining in his final years that "Now I am forced to put my beautiful machines in the corner of my room."

Papin first proposed his steam piston in 1690, and in 1695 seems to have built a clumsy model which nevertheless had all the essentials. The steam, led from a boiler, raised a piston in a vertical cylinder, thus operating a pump. Then as the cylinder cooled and the steam condensed the piston fell back under its own weight. But it was Thomas Savery of England who first put a practical steam pump into use. His patent dated from 1698, and included the condensing of the steam in the cylinder by means of an application of cold water. In 1702 he actually began manufacturing his pumps commercially. In 1712 Thomas Newcomen and John Calley invented another steam engine for use in the mines. Savery's engine had been a simple suction pump. Newcomen's, condensing the steam by spraying water directly into the cylinder, operated a separate pump by means of a walking beam. With James Watt's engine of 1770, with its separate condenser, the modern steam engine was born.

The eighteenth century also saw great progress in electrical studies. Newton's idea of action at a distance must have helped the savants to understand the strange new phenomena, for after all electrified amber attracted bits of paper from a distance, a magnet similarly pulled iron filings towards itself, and a steeple, it was discovered, actually attracted the light-

ning which was about to strike it. Many curious properties of electrified bodies had already been noted by William Gilbert, private physician to Queen Elizabeth of England, who listed many substances that behaved like amber when rubbed, calling them "electrics" (the origin of our modern term). Gilbert had noticed a certain relation between magnetism and electricity, and he claimed that electrification was due to the emanation of a fluid released by the rubbing, which flowed back into the body when the electricity was discharged.

The first machine to generate an electrical charge was built in 1660 by that vigorous scientist, Otto von Guericke. The friction machine of Guericke was much improved by Francis Hawkesbee in 1709, who substituted a rotating glass globe for the original sulphur ball. About 1729 Stephen Gray discovered the principle of conduction, or the actual flow of electricity, and distinguished between conductors and non-conductors by discovering that he could send charges through a variety of materials such as string, wood, and reed. He also noted that the brush discharge emitted from a point was different from the electric spark.

Meanwhile electric machines multiplied. Mechanical rubbers took the place of hands in the 1740's, and later the disc machine—Ramsden's machine of 1766 was the best known—took the place of the old glass globe machine, while metal collectors concentrated the charge for transfer to other bodies. By 1775 the electric machine was a sophisticated bit of apparatus. Its rotating disc was often driven by a gear mechanism, it was mounted on glass supports, and was furnished with the standard collecting brushes

76   A late 18th century laboratory table is set up with apparatus of various kinds for experiments in static electricity. A battery of Leyden jars, at the left, provides the necessary electric charge.

77-84 *(next page) A by-product of the remarkable scientific advances of the 17th and 18th centuries was the intense interest displayed by the educated public in things scientific. Unlike our day, it took the form of gadgetry, of demonstrations, of tricks and games making use of the new knowledge. Illustrated here are various diversions and pieces of apparatus culled from "Récréations de physique," published in Paris in 1749. The range is wide. "Amusemens de l'eau" (77, 80) includes fountains and other hydraulic apparatus. "Amusemens de l'air" (78) features an air gun. Things that can be done with magnets (79, 82, 84) include a question-and-answer game (84). Fireworks (81) are also depicted, as well as miscellaneous objects (83).*

or combs; the contacts were covered with an amalgam of mercury and lead and the wheel itself with waxed taffeta to prevent the escape of electricity. The Duke of Chaulnes' machine had a wheel five feet in diameter and could produce sparks 22 inches long.

The Leyden jar, a device for storing electricity, was invented in 1745 by the Dutchman Van Musschenbroek and popularized by the Abbé Nollet, an indefatigable monk with a scientific bent who was probably the earliest and best of the popularizers of science. He gave lessons in his laboratory not only to students and philosophers but also to a great many ladies and gentlemen of quality who at this time were passionately interested in the mysteries of nature. In 1738 the Abbé Nollet published a course of instruction in experimental physics, the preface of which is almost a book in itself. "Physics," he said, "is not, as it used to be, a senseless collection of unjustifiable arguments or of visionary systems. Today, nothing is trusted that cannot be seen, and reason judges only on the basis of the results of experience." In another part of his book, Nollet regretted "our habit up to now of leaving young people in ignorance of the fundamental principles of physics, which explains why such a large number of well-educated people insist upon believing in all sorts of popular fallacies. Since they are a prey to the most ridiculous fears, they are ready to be taken in by almost any fake marvel or quackery that has been cooked up to hoodwink them." Are we in any better shape today?

Among the many experiments in static electricity during the eighteenth century, Benjamin Franklin's hazardous adventure with the kite stands out. In June of 1752 he launched a kite equipped with a point and a conductor into a thunderstorm to test his theory that lightning was actually electricity. Franklin was fortunately unharmed, as was Dalibard, who had tried the same experiment in France a few months earlier. But when Professor Richmann of St. Petersburg tried it the next year, he was killed. Thus was born the lightning rod.

In 1767, Joseph Priestley, after one of his many electrical experiments, made this startling suggestion: "May we not infer from this experiment, that the attraction of electricity is subject to the same laws with that of gravitation, and is therefore according to the [inverse] squares of the distances?..." Somewhat later Charles Coulomb, who with his torsion balance established the fundamental laws of electrostatics and magnetism, demonstrated more conclusively that electrical attraction was the same as the gravitational force—at least as it was conceived by Newton. "Just as matter attracts matter," he wrote, "in direct proportion to mass, so electrical charges attract and repel in proportion to the product of their densities."

Considering how new was the field, the eighteenth century physicists had already come a long way in electrical theory. With mathematical analysis they might have been able to discover the true nature of electricity. Their magnificent electrical machines, of which the most sophisticated was that of Wimshurst, were prototypes of the famous modern Van de Graaff generator, and thus were distant ancestors of the first great atom smashing machines which appeared between the wars, the high voltage accelerators.

77

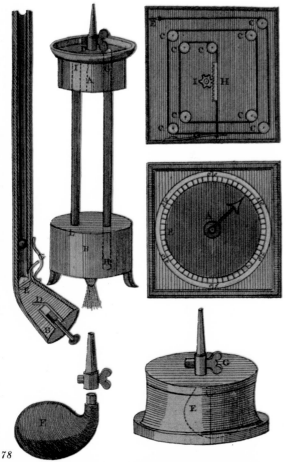

78

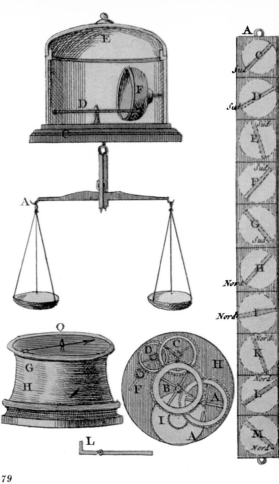

79

80

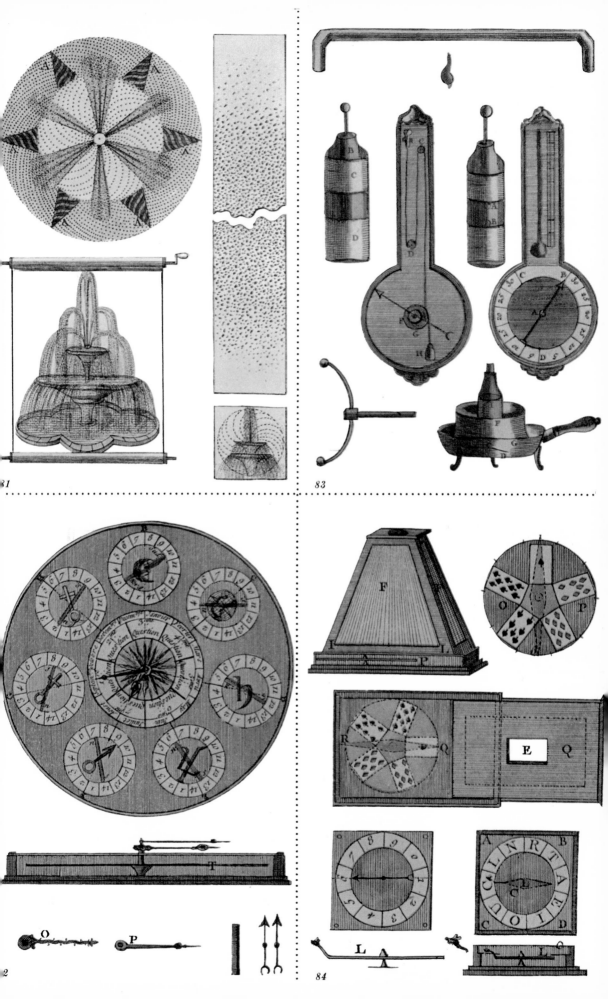

81

83

2

84

85   A 19th century conversation by
"string telephone." The vibrations of the man's
voice are carried from the "mouth piece"
along the string to the "receiver."
Sound wave patterns are superimposed.

Typical of nineteenth century physics was the increasing interdependence of science and technology. The scientists, availing themselves of all sorts of new technical developments, began to display a doctrinaire intolerance, an almost pathetic self-confidence, which was summed up in the dominating credo of the period, the belief that "success justifies the theory." The outstanding and even spectacular developments in electricity and optics, for instance, were based upon theories that were not only questionable but in some cases totally wrong. Never had logic been more confounded: truth was not only deduced from false premises, but error as well.

Yet the theoretical progress of nineteenth century physics was not necessarily smothered by this radical scientism. It was quite the opposite; for along with the more ambitious and naive minds a group of modest and painstaking scientists, with little thought of private gain, pursued ends which did great honor to the human intellect. In general mechanics and optics, for instance, the French physicist Léon Foucault studied the principle of the gyroscope with little idea of putting his invention to practical use. Leaving to others the quest for riches and glory, he concentrated upon his famous experimental demonstration of the rotation of the earth. Carried out in 1851, it depended upon a hitherto neglected fact: the invariance of the plane in which a pendulum swings. "If the oscillations continue for long enough," explained the inventor, "the steady rotation of the earth from west to east will become evident in contrast with the fixed plane of oscillation of the pendulum which, relative to

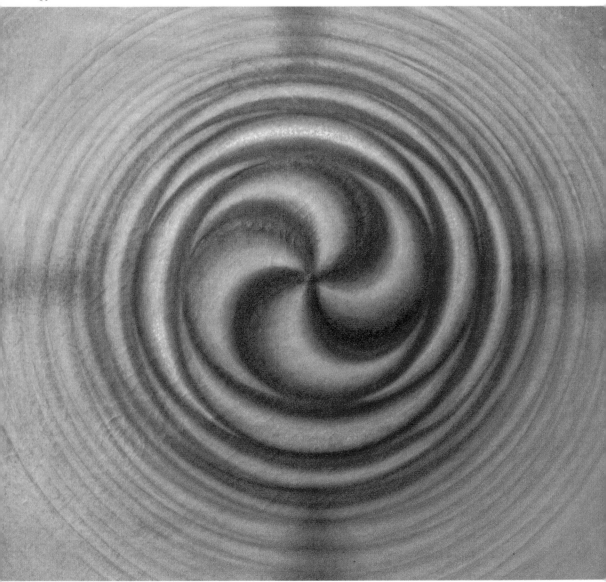

86-87 *Two paintings visualizing the phenomenon of interference in light. When two waves or vibrations of any kind meet, their mutual effect upon one another is called interference. In the case of light, interference causes lines or bands, either light and dark or of various colors. With sound waves, when the crest of one wave coincides with the trough of another, they cancel each other out—producing silence! If, however, the crests of two sound waves are superposed, the sound is amplified. Interference effects in light were first studied by Thomas Young in 1801, then demonstrated conclusively, in terms of the wave theory of light, by Fresnel around 1815.*

87

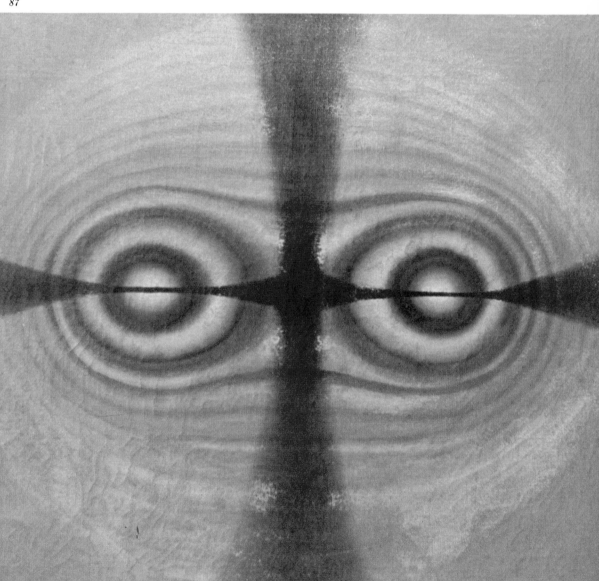

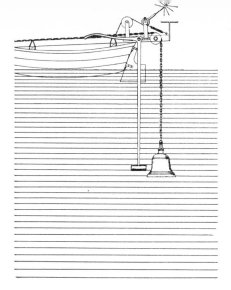

88　*Experiment on the conduction of sound through water, 1827. The two boats were stationed on opposite sides of the Lake of Geneva. When the hammer struck the bell (left) the light on the boat was turned on. Observers across the lake (right) then measured the time elapsed between the flashing of the light and the arrival of the sound at their boat.*

the earth, should rotate at the same rate as the apparent movement of the celestial sphere.''

The pendulum in the Pantheon in Paris was 67 meters long and carried a ball weighing 28 kilos. At the end of five minutes a deviation of one degree was already perceptible, and after thirty hours the plane of oscillation had turned through a complete circle. This research led to the development of the modern gyroscope.

Sadi Carnot was another high-minded and brilliant scientist, little known in his own time, who laid the foundations of the science of thermodynamics in an unassuming leaflet of 1824 entitled *Reflections on the Motive Power of Fire and Machines for its Exploitation.* His work contributed to an understanding of the steam, hot air, gasoline, and diesel engines and, rather paradoxically, to the refrigerator. Carnot himself, however, was of a shy and meditative nature and certainly had no idea of the importance of his discoveries. Although our rocket motors and atomic power stations of today generate energy in amounts far beyond Carnot's wildest dreams, they still depend for their operation upon Carnot's two fundamental laws, published when he was scarcely 30 years of age, which state the relationship between temperature and motive power, and the principle of the conservation of energy. Carnot led an obscure life, dying at 36 of cholera, and was soon forgotten. But his works were resurrected, and today his fame is world-wide.

Carnot's pioneering work in thermodynamics was carried forward by the English physicist James Joule, who investigated at different times the transformation of mechanical energy into heat, then of mechanical energy into electrical

energy, and finally, of electrical energy, first back into mechanical energy and later also into heat. The amount of mechanical energy equivalent to one calorie of heat was estimated by him to be 4.28 joules (using the unit of energy which has been named in his honor).

In the meantime the study of electricity had been making great strides. From the middle of the eighteenth century through the early nineteenth century the idea of electricity as a fluid dominated the field. It was a false idea and yet, paradoxically, it produced great advances. But how many fluids were there? As early as the 1730's Charles DuFay had postulated two different kinds of electricity, the resinous and the vitreous (named for their generators). In 1759 Robert Symmer of the Royal Society of London divided electricity into two fluids, one positive, the other negative. On the two-fluid theory Coulomb preferred to keep an open mind, confining himself "to presenting, with the minimum of hypothesis, the results of calculation and of experiment." Benjamin Franklin finally resolved the dilemma with his new one-fluid theory, in which the positive and negative features of electricity were merely two aspects of the same property.

The idea of a fluid, of something flowing, was also helpful in Alessandro Volta's invention of the "pile" or battery in 1796, which for the first time produced a continuous electric current. Napoleon was so impressed by the invention that he presented a 600-section Volta pile to the Ecole Polytechnique with which it was possible to carry out a number of experiments on the decomposition of water and on the magnetic, chemical, and heating properties of electricity.

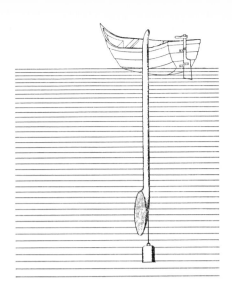

The analogy, again, between the displacement of electrified corpuscles and the flow of a river led Georg Ohm to publish in 1826, in his *Mathematical Theory of the Electric Circuit*, his famous law which states that the amount of current in a circuit is directly proportional to the electric pressure and inversely proportional to the resistance of the conductor. The concept of electrical resistance was one of the most fruitful ever proposed, and the applications of Ohm's law have been legion. For instance, it explains how the heat generated in an electric circuit depends on the nature of the conductor, its length, and its cross section. In much the same way a river flows quietly when its bed is wide and straight, but in a narrow winding gorge it tumbles turbulently. Such an analogy, of course, is not an argument; but the law itself has survived all experimental tests.

Meanwhile the concept of electricity as a fluid had continued to promote new developments such as Hans Christian Oersted's discovery of the magnetic effect of an electric current. It had been known for some time that lightning could magnetize iron, so that it seemed reasonable to suppose that electricity could produce magnetism. But it was pure chance that led this Danish scientist in 1820 to observe, when he was lecturing on the heating of a wire by an electric current, that the needle of a compass that lay nearby was swinging sideways in response to the current. Soon thereafter the French scientist François Arago, witnessing a demonstration of Oersted's experiment in Geneva, reported the results in detail to the Academy of the Sciences at Paris on the 4th and 11th of September, 1820. Pondering this

information, the fertile mind of André-Marie Ampère drew the necessary conclusions; and on the 18th of September he himself addressed the Academy. As he reported it: "I followed by giving some details about my idea that magnets owe their unique properties to electric currents which circulate in the plane perpendicular to their axis, and about the similar current which according to my proposition must flow in the earth itself. In this way all the phenomena of magnetism were deemed to be simply the effect of electric currents."

From this moment Ampère's experiments and theories followed each other in quick succession, and by 1822 he had firmly established, by experiment and quantitative analysis, what might be called the science of electricity in motion, or electrodynamics. His conclusions were finally embodied in 1825 in one of the most celebrated and influential memoirs in the history of science. Ampère also invented the electromagnet—his brilliant intuition leading him to predict that the coil would behave in every way just like a magnet—and experimented with an early electromagnetic telegraph.

The way had now been prepared for the next crucial step, the discovery, independently and almost simultaneously, of electromagnetic induction by Michael Faraday in England in 1831 and by Joseph Henry in the United States. Both observed that the alternation of an electric current through a circuit would momentarily "induce" another current in a totally independent circuit nearby. Moreover, the motion of a magnet near a closed circuit would also give rise to an electric current. Here was a logical development of electricity in motion, one that

89 Illustrations from a mid-19th century German treatise on physics showing the decomposition of a ray of light when projected through a prism as well as differently shaped openings. Studies of the spectrum based on the wave theory of light were initiated by the French physicist, Fresnel, early in the 19th century.

90 Hand painted diagram, from an 1830 English study of colors, illustrating the formation of the full spectrum on black ribbons when viewed through a prism.

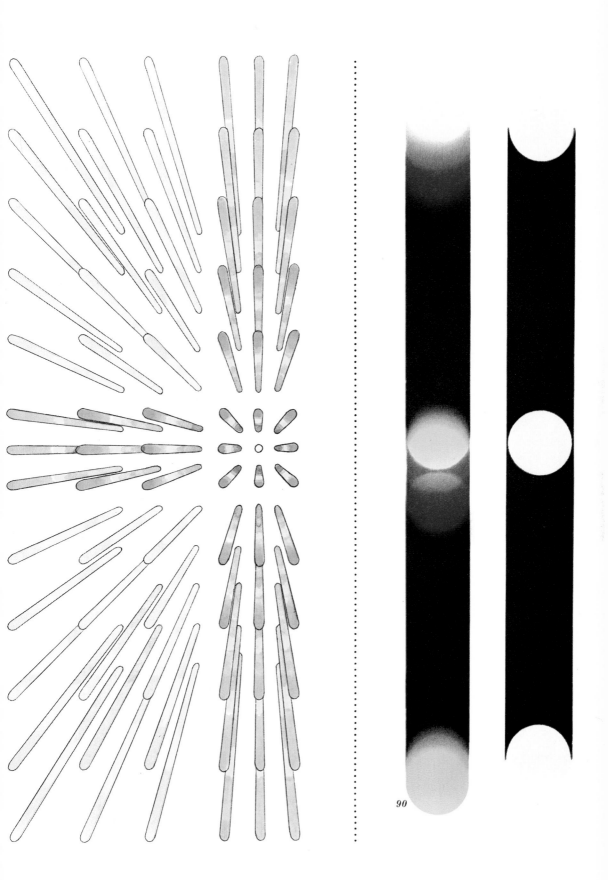

90

63

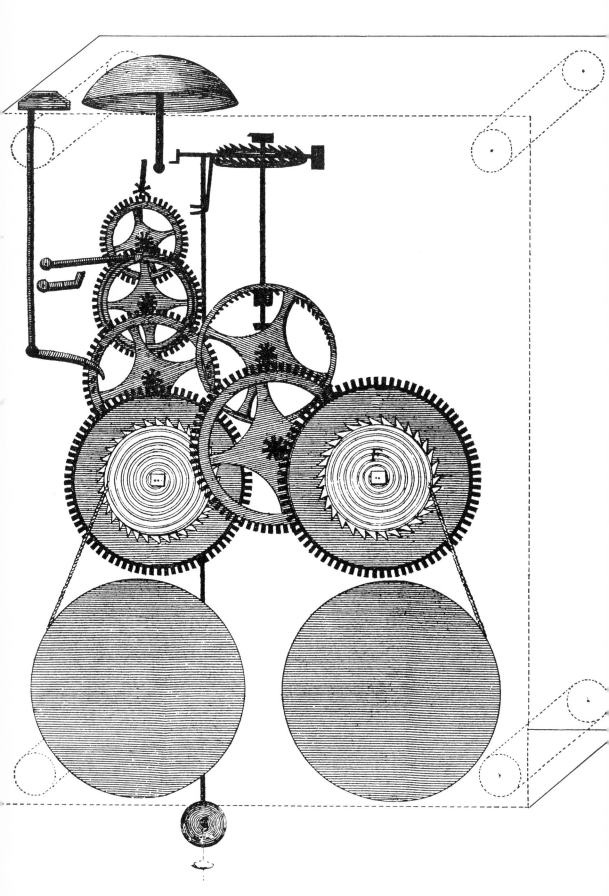

led directly to the invention of the dynamo and the electric motor. The dynamo of Zénobe Gramme, the first with real industrial potential, appeared in 1871—and could even double as a rather weak electric motor. It is curious to note that some of these early generators, like that of Pixii (1832), produced alternating currents—like our huge industrial giants of today—but Gramme and his contemporaries put all their energies into developing a source of direct current. It is surprising to realize, moreover, that many industrial leaders were distinctly hostile to the new invention and took to rounding up scientists who would agree to swear that the machine had absolutely no future. In a sense they were right, for the industrial usefulness of the dynamo depended upon the development of a system for the transmission of electrical current over long distances without crippling power losses. This became possible with the introduction of alternating current systems by George Westinghouse and others in the 1880's.

In the meantime Sir Joseph W. Swan in England—after experimenting since 1848—and the American inventor Thomas Edison had produced the first practical commercial electric lights with a carbon filament in 1878 and 1879. But Edison stuck to direct current. When the "great power fight" of the 1880's was resolved in favor of alternating current, electric power began to take its rightful place in industry as well as in the humble operations of every household.

The discoveries of the great Michael Faraday extended far beyond electricity. In 1823, for instance, he was the first to liquify chlorine as well as sulphurdioxide and ammonia. By 1845 he had liquified ethylene and phosphine under pressure. Today, thanks to the new methods developed by that neglected scientist, Georges Claude, all gases have been liquified and most even solidified. Dewar obtained liquid hydrogen in 1898 and in 1908 Kamerling Onnes was able to liquify helium. Helium in its solid state was obtained by Keeson in 1926.

These were striking achievements; but the theoretical advance was equally important. The kinetic theory of gases was first proposed by Daniel Bernoulli in 1738. In 1809 Gay-Lussac showed that gases always combine according to simple ratios, and in 1811 the Italian physicist Avogadro formulated his famous hypothesis: that equal volumes of different gases, under the same conditions of pressure and temperature, contain the same number of molecules. The kinetic theory of gases was confirmed by the experiments of many scientists. Eventually it became possible to calculate the actual dimensions of the atoms of which any given gas was composed.

In a sense the nineteenth century can be described as the century of waves. Following an already well-established tradition, the scientists tried to explain everything in terms of waves. In acoustics the task was a straightforward one, and Hermann von Helmholtz had no difficulty in measuring the frequencies corresponding to the various notes of the musical scale. It was also easy enough to establish that air was essential for the propagation of sound, because when an electric bell was placed inside a vacuum it became inaudible to the experimenter. But the speed of sound still had to be established. This problem had been tackled many times—by Gassendi and Father Mersemme, by the physicists of the Academy of

92   *Aneroid barometer made in Paris, 1887.*

93   *Instrument built in the late 18th century by Haldat for experiments with pressure of the atmosphere.*

94   *An "absolute" barometer of 1870, with centigrade thermometer.*

95   *A thermometer-barometer combination of the 18th century.*

98

96

96 Hygrometer with turning figurines,
    (used to measure the humidity of the air).
97 Thermometer by Aristide Janvier, 1833.
98 Bétalli barometer, around 1830.

99

99   Another "absolute barometer," 1878.
100 Barometer of the type built by the
     Bréguet family, from an advertisement,
     late 19th century.

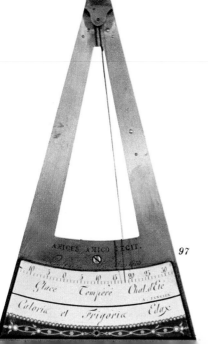

97

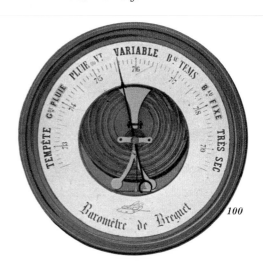

100

Florence, by Boyle, Halley and Huygens—but the results remained contradictory. In 1822 the problem was officially re-examined by the Bureau of Longitudes at Paris in the presence of many scientists, including François Arago, who was a strong advocate of the study of wave motion.

For these experiments two batteries of artillery were used, and as the measurements were made in two directions the uncertainty due to wind was greatly reduced. Moreover the excellent chronometers, made by Bréguet, ensured precise measurement of elapsed time. Under these conditions the result obtained for the velocity of sound was 333 meters per second at a temperature of 0° centigrade, a figure which was corrected during the First World War and now stands at 331 meters per second. The interference of sound waves was also studied at this time, after which it became an accepted fact that the correct combination of two sound waves results in... silence!

In optics analogous experiments were carried out by a physicist of real genius, Augustin Fresnel. Daring and subtle in his thinking, Fresnel died at the early age of 39. On his deathbed he expressed his sorrow in moving terms: "I would like to have lived longer because I feel that in the inexhaustible gold mine of science there are many problems whose secrets I might have had the good fortune to reveal." It was Fresnel who took up and developed the ideas of Huygens on light as a wave motion in the aether. After 1814 Fresnel began to apply the theory of aether waves to the phenomenon of aberration, and in 1818, encouraged by Arago and Ampère, he wrote his celebrated memoir on diffraction for the Parisian Academy of the Science's prize for that year. Unfortunately, most of the Academy's members still held to the corpuscular theory of light and were stoutly opposed to Fresnel's novel ideas. Those who prided themselves on their common-sense, for instance, were profoundly shocked by his famous experiment with a slit and a mirror which demonstrated the reality of optical interference, that is, that two beams of light may mutually destroy each other. Surely it was in poor taste to pretend, as Arago had quipped, that "light added to light can produce darkness"?

In the end, however, Fresnel's memoir (which included a section on the celebrated Fresnel integrals that make it possible to account for the fringes of light and darkness observed at the edge of a shadow) was accepted and printed by the Academy—although "with considerable delay." It must be said that this was due in part to the valiant efforts of Arago, who by a series of masterly experiments succeeded in silencing most of the unbelievers. It was time to bow to progress and the members of the Academy, perhaps deciding that discretion was the better part of valor, gave in without further discussion.

Somewhat later—in 1849 to be exact—Hippolyte Fizeau used his toothed wheel to measure the velocity of light. He obtained a velocity of 315,000 kilometers per second with an estimated maximum error of 500 kilometers per second. Using a rotating mirror, Léon Foucault the next year improved Fizeau's results, finding the value of 298,197 kilometers per second. Finally Newcomb in 1882 obtained a value of 299,860 kilometers per second, with a margin of error of only 30 kilometers per

second, which was very close to the modern value of 299,973 kilometers per second.

On the basis of these experiments, as well as many others less spectacular but equally convincing, the physicists of the time felt no further inclination to doubt the existence of the aether. It was generally considered that the aether offered an ideal medium for the propagation of all sorts of energy in the form of waves. But while in the case of sound the oscillations in the medium were known to be longitudinal, in the case of light they had been proved to run in the opposite manner, that is, transversely. This had been established by Fresnel in the 1820's as a result of his beautiful experiments on polarized light. However (as was shrewdly observed even at the time) for waves to propagate at this velocity the aether would have to be 10,000 times as rigid as steel. This was of course a weighty objection; nevertheless it was pretty much disregarded. In fact the net result was to stimulate an even more frantic search for a direct experimental demonstration of the existence of the aether. Heinrich Hertz was among those who caught the fever. Stimulated by the theoretical work of James Clerk Maxwell, who as early as 1864 predicted the existence of electromagnetic waves travelling at the speed of light through the aether, Hertz started a systematic investigation of the possibility of electrical waves propagating in the aether in the same way as light.

In 1888, just after his 31st birthday, Hertz published his famous paper on "The Propagation of Electrical Energy in Space." His experiments, carried out with the help of a spark gap driven by an induction coil, enabled him to observe induced sparks in another electrical circuit, close by but totally separated from the first one. Realizing that this "induction at a distance" was due to the propagation of the long-sought electrical waves, he demonstrated, as a further step, the phenomenon of interference. Moreover, by determining the distance between the nodes and antinodes he was able to measure the wave length of the radiation and so calculated the velocity of propagation—which proved to be equal to that of light. These "Hertzian waves," later known as radio waves, seemed to mean little to their discoverer. "I am convinced," he wrote, "that the Hertzian waves will never be of any practical value."

Nevertheless in 1890 Edouard Branly developed a detector called the coherer, operating with iron filings, with which he was able to detect the Hertzian waves "at a distance of more than 20 meters, although the spark generator was operating in a laboratory separated from the receiver by three large rooms so that the sound of the sparks could not even be heard." The rest of the story of wireless and radio is well known: the invention of the electrolytic detector by Vreland, and the magnetic detector by Guglielmo Marconi. In 1904 John Fleming developed the two-element, or diode, vacuum tube, which was vastly improved with Lee De Forest's triode, or audion of 1907. Commercial broadcasting began in the United States in 1920 and in England in 1921. It is curious to note, in closing, the vast social and economic changes that have been brought about by a discovery considered by its inventor to have no practical value—unless it was the detection of the elusive aether, which after all does not exist.

101 Experimental verification of the laws of sound reflection in 1882. Sound waves from watch (ticking at right) are received full strength at reflector (left).
102 (next page) Table of weights and measures.

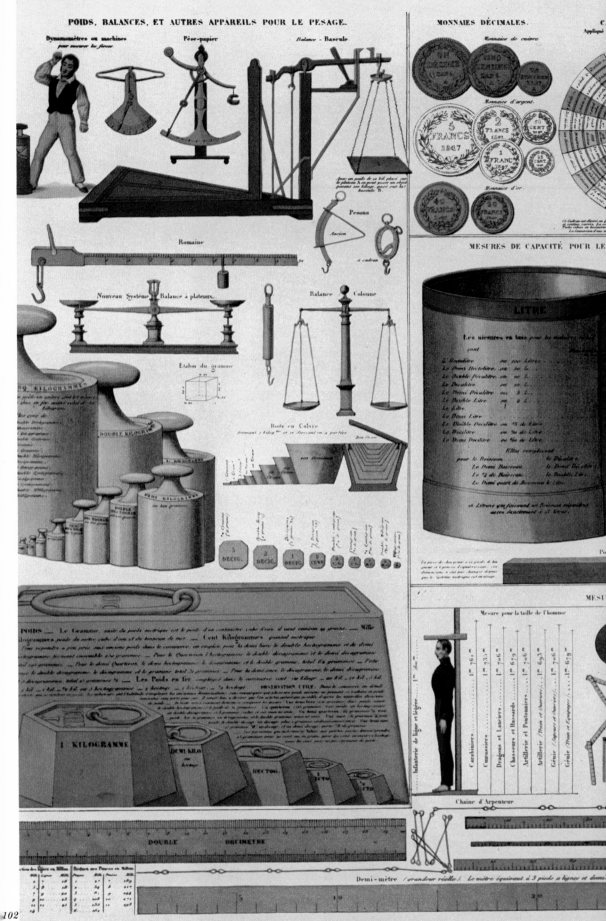

POIDS, BALANCES, ET AUTRES APPAREILS POUR LE PESAGE.

MONNAIES DÉCIMALES.

MESURES DE CAPACITÉ POUR LE

LITRE

DOUBLE DÉCIMÈTRE

Demi-mètre (grandeur réelle). Le mètre équivaut à 3 pieds 8 lignes et demi.

103

*103-104   Diagrams from the works of James Clerk Maxwell,
whose theory of electromagnetic radiations
at the speed of light, verified by Hertz in 1888,
led to radio and many other aspects of modern physics.*

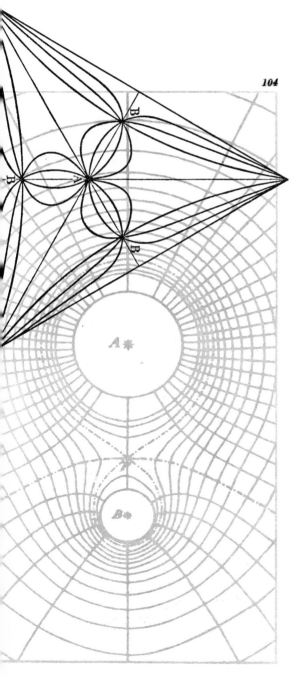

104

It was the hope of nineteenth century physics to be able to provide a simple explanation for all aspects of matter and energy. Certain established principles were considered inviolable: the conservation of mass, the unique and indestructible character of the atom, and the propagation of all kinds of radiant energy as waves in the aether. One great objective was to set up a kind of periodic table of radiations, starting with the lowest frequencies (at that time, sound) and ending with the very high frequencies corresponding to wireless waves and light. In 1865 James Clerk Maxwell published his electromagnetic theory of light which showed convincingly that light could be described as an electromagnetic wave. As a result, it was possible to suppose that the electromagnetic waves of Hertz differed from visible light only in the frequency or the wave length. Experiment was to show in fact that electromagnetic waves could be reflected and refracted in much the same way as light.

One could envisage a final solution to all the problems of physics in an association of the idea of wave motion with the general principles of mechanics and electricity. But this comfortable synthesis was to prove only a dream; for little by little reports came in of unexpected phenomena which contradicted many of the beautiful certainties in which physicists had put their trust. The discovery, for instance, of cathode rays and of radioactivity followed each other within a few months. Improved apparatus played a major part in such advances. For example, the phenomena associated with the conduction of electricity through gases had always been of interest; but now the induction

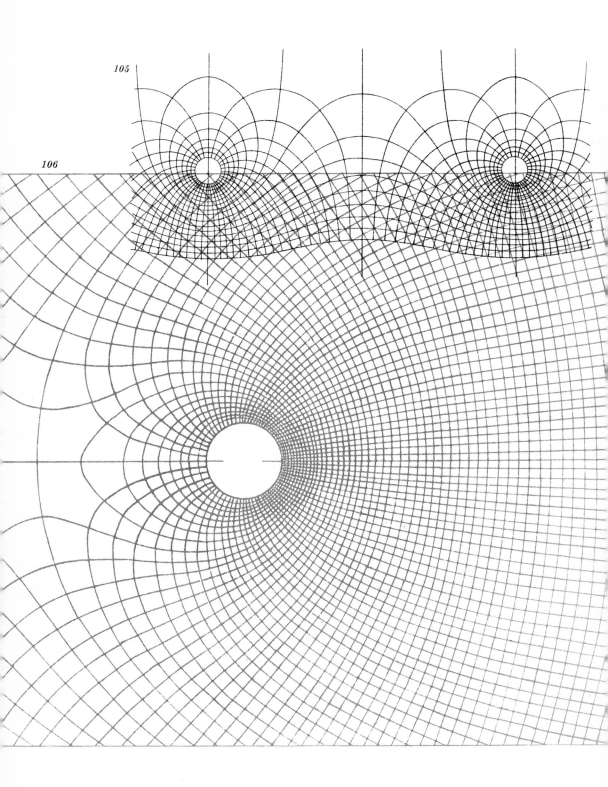

105

106

105-107 Lines of force in magnetic fields, as visualized in the works of James Clerk Maxwell. In 1865 Maxwell concluded, after studying electromagnetic phenomena, that an oscillating or alternating electromagnetic disturbance should project electromagnetic waves through space at the speed of light. Some 20 years later this prediction was experimentally verified by Heinrich Hertz, who with a brass ring actually detected electromagnetic waves from a spark discharge. He also showed that these "Hertzian waves," soon to be called radio waves, could be bent, reflected, or refracted like light. The discovery of the nature of electromagnetic radiations, which include light, heat, X-rays and natural radiation, opened the way to radio, TV, radar, and the atom bomb.

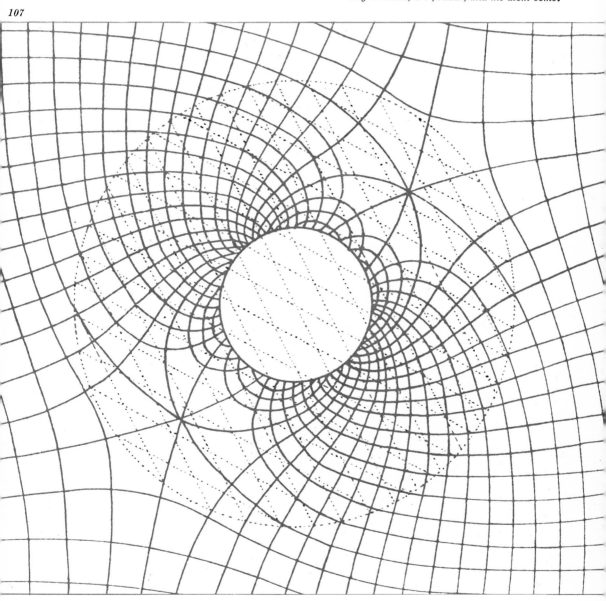

108

coil invented by Ruhmkorff had replaced the old influence machines, while in vacuum technology excellent new pumps were available. Moreover, the necessary glass tubes in which to create the vacuum were also to be had, thanks to the work of a German physicist named Heinrich Geissler, who learned how to blow tubes of many shapes with metal contacts sealed into them. Consequently it was now possible to investigate electric discharges in gases at low pressure.

A number of scientists, including the illustrious Faraday, had made such investigations, but it was left to Pflücker, De La Rive, and the French physicists Masson, Fizeau, Foucault, and Rayer to push ahead in the field. Rayer in particular noticed in 1868 that the spectrum emitted from a discharge in low pressure hydrogen was the same as that of the solar protuberances. An even more sensational discovery, however, was made by Sir William Crookes, who in 1878 began to study the passage of electric current through tubes of gas at extremely low pressures. He was astonished to find that under these conditions no light was emitted from the interior of the bulb "but that the walls were lit up by a brilliant green light." Crookes showed that this effect was due to a characteristic radiation emitted by the negative electrode, or "cathode." These rays travelled in straight lines across the tube and any object in their path became hot and luminescent, and was also subject to measurable force. All the evidence suggested that the objects were being bombarded by particles travelling at tremendous speeds. Despite the primacy of wave motion in the ideas of his time, Crookes had the temerity to

suggest the bright green light emitted by the walls of his tube could be explained by an intense bombardment by molecules of matter. His analysis was correct—except for the size of the projectiles—and he thus reintroduced into physics the idea of corpuscular emission. Perhaps Newton had been right after all!

It was not long before all the laboratories of Europe had equipped themselves with apparatus for studying the Crookes radiation. About 1880 Hertz showed that the cathode rays, as they are now called, could traverse thin metal foils placed in their path, and in 1892 Lenard succeeded in bringing the rays out into the air by providing his bulb with a thin metal window. This seemed at first to eliminate the hypothesis of corpuscular emission because it was not expected that a beam of molecules could penetrate a metal wall, which was after all thousands of molecules thick. But what else could they be? In 1895 Jean Perrin showed that the cathode rays carried a negative charge. It was J.J. Thomson in 1897 who first estimated their mass and thus established the existence of the fundamental carrier of electricity, the electron. In 1910 the American physicist, Robert A. Millikan, after several years of experimentation, succeeded in measuring the charge on the electron, thus providing proof of the atomic theory of matter.

In 1895 Wilhelm Roentgen, who was also carrying out some experiments with cathode rays, noticed by chance that the Crookes tube was emitting another type of radiation. These new rays behaved in an incredible manner. Travelling in straight lines, they could go right through solid objects, making it possible to

109

photograph the bones of a man through the living flesh. This news electrified the laboratories of the world; and in fact there was no difficulty in repeating the experiment. All that was required was a Crookes tube, an induction coil, and a photographic plate wrapped in black paper. A fluorescent screen covered with the appropriate mineral powder was a useful accessory. Within a few months of Roentgen's discovery the medical profession began using the tube in many different ways. Radiography—or X-ray photography—became all the rage, and there was no shortage of guinea pigs.

Two important aspects of these mysterious radiations, however, were completely unknown: the insidious dangers which they present for those who dally too long in their vicinity, and the physical reasons for their origin. Roentgen himself believed that they were "longitudinal vibrations in the aether." But first, from which part of the Crookes tube was the radiation coming? Henri Poincaré put forward the suggestion that the X-ray emission had something to do with the fluorescence of the glass under the bombardment of the cathode rays. He was both right and wrong; the glass walls were, in fact, the source of the mysterious radiation, but the emission had nothing whatever to do with the fluorescence itself. Emission of X-rays could be observed equally well, or in fact better, from metals which did not fluoresce at all. But nevertheless, Poincaré's apparently trivial remark was to lead to the discovery of natural radioactivity.

If Poincaré's hypothesis were true, other naturally fluorescent substances, for example potassium uranium sulphate, might also emit X-rays. Henri Becquerel decided to investigate this idea. Early in 1896 he placed a photographic plate in a black cardborad box and fixed to the outside two plates of potassium uranium sulphate. Between one of them and the box he placed a piece of money and to stimulate the fluorescence exposed the whole apparatus to the sun. On developing the plate, Henri Becquerel was pleased to find an image corresponding to the positions of the two plates as well as a shadow cast by the piece of silver. Poincaré's hypothesis seemed to have been brilliantly confirmed; but a surprise was in store!

Becquerel prepared another experiment, but the sun was slow to appear, and while waiting he put the whole apparatus away in a dark drawer. On March 1, 1896, prompted perhaps by impatience rather than curiosity, he decided to make sure that his photographic plate was still intact. He placed it in the developer and found to his astonishment that the penetrating radiation had already left its mark. Incredible though it seemed, the evidence was unmistakable: the dark patch which reproduced the shape of the two uranium crystals was intersected by the shadow of a thin copper cross that had been placed under them. As an emitter of X-rays, the uranium salt was just as effective in the darkness of the drawer as it had been in sunlight: fluorescence had nothing to do with the phenomenon. Displaying a sure grasp of the situation, Becquerel was soon able to announce that the new radiation was a characteristic atomic property of uranium, quite independent of its chemical composition. This theory, received at first with scepticism, was soon confirmed by J. J. Thomson. Gradually but

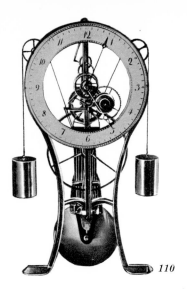

110

111

inevitably the truth was established. The salts of uranium behaved like naturally occurring Crookes tubes: but no one was able to offer an explanation for this curious property.

In 1882 Pierre Curie was appointed head of experimental studies at the School of Physics and Chemistry in Paris. At this time he and his wife, Marie, were unknown to the public, but had already been recognized among scientists for their brilliance. Pierre Curie was specializing primarily in crystallography while his wife had the idea of studying the properties of uranium, its various compounds, and the minerals in which it was found. Some of these showed an activity even greater than that of uranium in the pure state, which seemed to indicate that they contained some unknown substance more active than uranium itself. Pierre Curie, postponing his crystallographic research, joined his wife in a concentrated effort to follow up her discovery. Not long afterwards Madame Curie was able to establish the existence of a new substance, polonium; and thus encouraged the pair were able to announce on 26th December, 1898, that they had discovered a new element, radium, which disintegrated spontaneously. It was later established that radium transformed itself into a whole series of radioactive elements, terminating finally in the inert metal, lead.

And thus a world-shaking fact was established that one element can indeed be transmuted into another, and in fact this process is occurring continuously in the natural world. It was not until 1904 that a professorship was created at the Sorbonne enabling Pierre Curie to teach the new science to which he had contributed so much. The early work of the Curies had been carried out under miserable conditions. As Curie himself wrote: "This shed with its asphalt floor, in which we passed the best and happiest years of our life, had as its only furniture some old tables of waxed pine on which I arranged our precious concentrates of radium obtained after years of fractionation. As we had no cupboard in which to put away the radioactive products, we set them out on tables or on planks, and I well remember the sense of excitement we felt when we used to enter our little world at night and saw on all sides the luminous products of our work glowing faintly in the darkness." The practical applications of the discoveries of Pierre and Marie Curie were destined to be of great importance, above all in medicine.

In 1912 the German physicist Max von Laue established the diffraction of X-rays, thus showing that they were similar to the well-known rays of visible light from which they differed only in the extremely high frequency of their vibration. This development would have given a new impetus to the concept of aether waves if it had not been for the discovery of the "quantum of action" by Max Planck in 1900 and its confirmation in Einstein's explanation of the so-called "photoelectric effect" (1905). But meanwhile the existence of the aether, and therefore of the aether waves, had been disproved many years before in a masterly experiment carried out in 1887 by Michelson and Morley. They set up an apparatus to investigate the effect on the velocity of light of the earth's motion through the aether. In 1881 Michelson had invented an interferometer of outstanding precision which he now put to use in an attempt either to confirm or to disprove the existence

110 *Chiming clock with openwork dial, 1817. The most important aspect of the mechanical clock is its regulating pendulum, studied by Leonardo da Vinci and Galileo and perfected by Huygens, who constructed his first pendulum clock in 1657.*
111 *Foucault's gyroscope. French physicist Léon Foucault invented the gyroscope in the mid-19th century.*
112 *Resonators of Hermann von Helmholtz, 19th century German physicist noted for his studies of sound. With his resonators Helmholtz was able to isolate simple (as opposed to compound) sounds, and established the frequencies of musical tones.*

112

of the aether. He argued that if the aether is really a stable medium able to carry the vibrational movements of the aether waves, including light and radio, then the velocity of the waves must be a velocity measured relative to the aether itself and not directly relative to the earth. This implied that by comparing the velocity of two light rays, one measured parallel, the other perpendicular to the direction of the earth's movement through the aether, the motion of the earth through the aether could be demonstrated, very much like the motion of a boat in a moving stream as seen by an observer standing on the bank. But as the velocity of the earth around the sun is only about 30 kilometers per second, a very sensitive apparatus was needed to establish the effect.

The apparatus of Michelson and Morley was indeed ingenious as well as sensitive, containing four mirrors, a source of light, and the precision interferometer mentioned above. The result of their experiment was absolutely negative. The earth's velocity of 30 kilometers a second did not have the slightest effect on the apparent velocity of light, which remained the same in every direction. The conclusion was that the aether did not exist, and it was this striking result that had a lot do to with the birth of the theory of relativity.

Albert Einstein was a man whose talents were primarily mathematical, but as physics is a science which can be formulated more and more in mathematical terms, the mathematical analysis of the principle of relativity was bound to lead to fruitful conclusions. Without the aether, no fixed point could be discovered in the whole universe. The experiment of Michelson and

Morley suggested, therefore, that the world in which we live is constructed in such a way that it is impossible for an observer in a moving system, by observations confined to that system, to establish the fact that he moves or to measure his own velocity. To this postulate, or rather to this axiom—for he took it as his starting point—Einstein added his second hypothesis, that the velocity of light always has the same value whatever the speed of translation of the apparatus with which we measure it.

Faced with such revolutionary ideas, it was immediately realized that the old laws of classical kinematics, as well as the old idea of space as a thing-in-itself, would have to be discarded. These considerations led Einstein to the exceedingly abstract idea of a space-time continuum. They also led to the general acceptance by physicists of a hypothesis proposed a century earlier by Bernhard Riemann, who had claimed that space had no meaning apart from the physical objects which it contained. Moreover, the constantly changing states of physical phenomena inevitably involved time in the definition of space. Today the general soudness of these concepts has been established in the domain of nuclear physics, furthermore there is sound experimental evidence to show that energy possesses a mass and that a material mass can be transformed into energy, as postulated by Einstein in his paper of 1905 which contained the key equation of the modern world, $E = mc^2$. A simple calculation shows that according to this formula a fantastic quantity of energy is locked up in one gram of ordinary matter.

About 1900 the great German physicist Max Planck put forth another radical idea, that

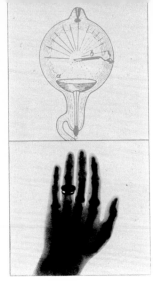

113

114

of the quantum, to explain the spectrum of light emitted by black bodies—one of those little riddles for which hitherto no solution had been found. The theories of Planck were expressed in such abstract mathematical terms that it is impossible to explain them fully here. The essential point is that, according to Planck, energy is basically discontinuous. Light is not found in nature as a sort of continuous flux, nor even less as a continuous fluid but, figuratively speaking, in little packets, or quanta. Planck, who had no desire to leave anything to guesswork, was careful to give exact figures for the size of these little packets. In C.G.S. units, the size is expressed by the almost infinitesimally small number 6.55×10^{-27}. This was the quantity which, multiplied by the frequency of the vibration, gave the amount of energy in the corresponding packet; and Planck claimed that it was impossible to obtain a smaller parcel. This basic number, now known as Planck's constant and designated by the letter "h", gives rise to the well-known formula, $E = h\nu$, where E is the energy and ν the frequency.

Planck's essential point was that the exchange of energy between matter and radiation must occur in finite lumps, or quanta. Radiation therefore has a discontinuous structure, as also the process of emission and absorption of light. As mentioned above, Einstein elaborated Planck's idea of quanta in his 1905 paper to explain the photoelectric effect (the ejection of electrons from metals by light), showing that light is not only emitted in quanta, but must also travel in quanta, thus affirming the reality of the photon in light. Physics was now faced with a great difficulty: if light consisted of a stream of photons, and electricity of a stream of electrons, how was one to understand the continuous structure which seemed necessary for wave motion?

It was not until 1924 that another scientific genius, Louis de Broglie, resolved the difficulty by a suggestion for which he was awarded the Nobel Prize. As he has himself remarked, the essential point was to find a subject for the verb "to wave." Louis de Broglie thought that the subject should be the electron itself, and not, as had been previously supposed, the all-too-metaphysical aether. "If this is the case," went on the great scientist, "one must suppose that material particles, the electron in particular, are accompanied and in a sense guided by a certain type of wave." This compromise solution forms the basis of the new theory called wave mechanics; and as a result of this new idea the paradox was resolved: "It is known today that the proton and the atomic nuclei, in which the positive charges in matter are concentrated, are also associated with a wave... and in this way the great barrier which has for so long separated the physics of matter from the physics of radiation seems to have been removed."

That is, at any rate, the implication of this new and abstract point of view. With the general acceptance of these ideas, physical reality, according to Sommerfeld, began to evaporate into a "pattern of mathematical equations." Thus science moves always further and further from a direct interpretation of the evidence of the five senses. Physics today requires a whole arsenal of mathematics for its logistic support; but the details of this development we must leave to our final chapter.

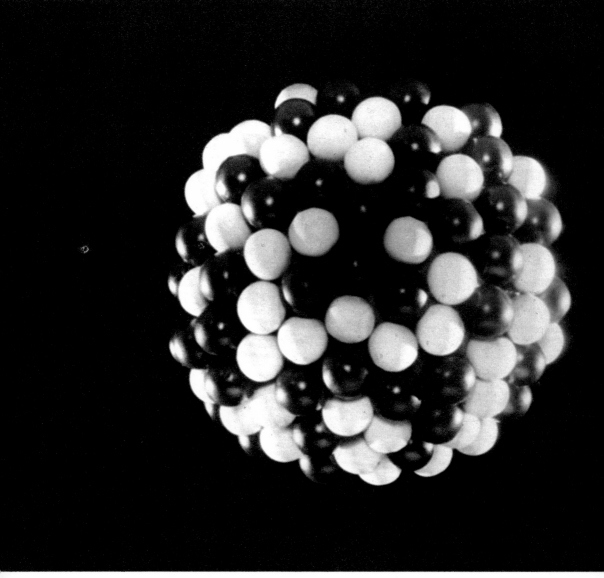

116 Model of the nucleus, the heart of
the atom, showing protons and neutrons.
The discovery and study of subatomic
particles is a feature of modern physics.
117 Albert Einstein, eminent physicist.

117

The great English physicist Joseph J. Thomson, following up Lenard's research on the cathode rays, discovered in 1897 that this strange radiation could be deflected by means of an electromagnet. On the assumption that the rays consisted of particles he was able to calculate their velocity, which proved to be close to the speed of light, and made preliminary measurements on their mass and charge. In fact he was able to establish that the ratio of charge to mass (e/m) was a constant for these particles, no matter what type of gas was used for setting up the electric discharge or kind of metal for the electrodes. "I cannot escape the conclusion," he said, "that we are dealing with charges of negative electricity carried by particles of matter."

Thus the idea of the electron, a fundamental unit of the atom, was born. In 1909-1910 Robert Millikan, at that time a professor at the University of Chicago, gave a further experimental demonstration of the existence of the electron. The apparatus he used was brilliantly simple. With the aid of an intense light source and a microscope he observed the motion of minute, electrically-charged droplets of oil, which were allowed to fall under the influence of gravity or made to rise by the application of a vertical electric field. From these observations it was possible to deduce the mass of the drop and also the electric charge on it. This proved to be always a multiple of the fundamental unit, the charge of the electron, which could thus be measured. Using Thomson's results, the mass of the electron could immediately be deduced. So the electron was by no means a figment of the imagination, even though, as Millikan pointed out, its diameter is roughly speaking ten

118

118 *Spherical discharger for measuring the voltage provided by the 3,000,000 volt shock generator, at the Ivry laboratory for atomic studies, 1942. Frederic Joliot, who, with his wife Irene Curie, did extensive research in nuclear physics, was for years director of this laboratory. Another device used there is the 900-kilovolt Greinacher generator, shown with accelerating tube (120).*
119 *The first atomic pile, or reactor, was built in a squash court at the University of Chicago in 1942.*

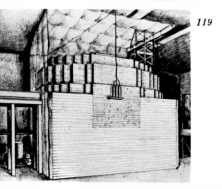

119

120

thousand million times smaller than that of a human hair.

The proton, the second fundamental unit of the atom, did not receive its official name until 1920, but its existence had been guessed at much earlier by the scientific world. In 1886, the German physicist Eugen Goldstein, mounting a cathode consisting of a perforated metal plate at the center of a Crookes tube, was able to observe not only the usual cathode rays, but also a new radiation which glowed with a clear golden light and which "penetrated the perforated plate and filled the whole space behind the cathode as far as the walls of the vessel." This radiation, which he called "canal rays," was nothing less than a stream of positively charged nuclei, left behind by the removal of an electron from the atom. The rays observed by Goldstein consisted of the nuclei of nitrogen. If the rarified gas in his tube had been hydrogen the color of the rays would have been pink and the nuclei would be protons, 1,840 times heavier than electrons, while carbon dioxide would have given a pale greenish light. In any case, Goldstein had given a superb demonstration of the ionization of the gas in his bulb, that is to say, the decomposition of its atoms into electrons (cathode rays) and charged nuclei (canal rays).

In 1910, J. J. Thomson, continuing his experiments on the gas discharge, directed these mysterious canal rays on to a fluorescent screen where they produced scintillations very similar to those of a beam of electrons. Deflecting the rays with both electric and magnetic fields, he was able to demonstrate that all particles of the same atomic weight produced a characteristic parabolic pattern on the screen. This led to a great surprise. Applying the new method of analysis to neon, Thomson observed that the gas traced a double parabola on the screen. "There is no doubt," he said, "that what we call neon is not a pure gas, but a mixture of two gases, one with an atomic weight of about 20 and the other with an atomic weight of about 22." Thus Thomson established the existence of isotopes, which were studied in much greater detail around 1920 by his assistant, F.W. Aston. Radioactive isotopes have now become an important by-product of the nuclear industry.

In the meantime the study of natural radioactivity was to lead to the transmutation of the elements, that cherished dream of the medieval alchemists. In 1903 Frederick Soddy and Sir William Ramsay had suggested that the alpha particles emitted from radium might actually be helium. In 1907 Ernest Rutherford of Cambridge was definitely able to identify the alpha particle with the nucleus of ionized helium—in other words helium which has lost its two satellite electrons. Still later, in 1919, Rutherford had the excellent idea of bombarding atoms of nitrogen with projectiles consisting of alpha particles, or helium nuclei, emitted at very high speed by an intensely radioactive source. The results were astonishing, for under bombardment the atoms of nitrogen had been transformed into oxygen. For the first time the atom had been broken apart and then reassembled to give another chemical element. Thus was transmutation—no longer an alchemist's fancy—finally accomplished. Rutherford had succeeded where Roger Bacon and Paracelsus had failed.

It is not difficult to imagine why, after such a discovery, the physicists hastened to disintegrate as many types of atoms as possible. But it is one thing to break down nitrogen; to disintegrate a heavy metal such as uranium is a much more complicated task. Thus the need for more powerful weapons led to the development step by step of the great linear accelerators, and then to those even more powerful "atom smashers" called cyclotrons, bevatrons, synchrotrons, and cosmotrons.

In the meantime, Niels Bohr had begun to study the structure of the atom. Rutherford, adopting a suggestion by Jean Perrin, had proposed an atom with the positive charge at the center and the electrons outside it. In his model of the atom Bohr assumed that the electrons were in motion in definite orbits, circling around the positively charged nucleus like the planets around the sun. He then set himself the task of establishing a rigorous mathematical theory to account for all the possible states of these particles. Above all, he succeeded in showing that in jumping from one "orbit" to another the electron must emit a quantum of energy. Thus the quantum theory of Planck had been brilliantly reconciled with the structure of the atom.

This rather simple idea of circular orbits, however, began to give rise to serious difficulties, so that by 1916 Sommerfeld, developing the ideas of Bohr, had begun to postulate orbits of elliptical shape and had used the principles of relativity to calculate the motions of the electrons. From this point on the theory became so complicated that it is impossible to explain

121

122

it without the help of a whole armory of mathematical formulae, including Schroedinger's equation and the Uncertainty Principle of Heisenberg. Suffice it to say that the end result was a geometrical construction which almost completely excluded the old idea of matter, with the electrons mere "clouds of probability" obeying only the laws of large numbers. Thus in the attempt to reconcile the continuous with the discontinuous a curious type of indeterminism, as in the ancient world, had been introduced into modern physics. In the words of Louis de Broglie, the great drama of contemporary physics had begun.

But to return to the disintegration of the atom, the principle of the transformation of mass into energy during atomic collisions, and vice versa, which had been predicted by Einstein, was to lead scientists along a path that was both exciting and dangerous. Around 1930 it began to be realized that during a transformation produced by nuclear bombardment a tremendous amount of energy would be liberated, because the final nuclei would have less mass than those with which one started. It has been calculated that the disappearance of one gram of matter brings about a liberation of energy sufficient to bring to an immediate boil 200 million liters of water. And this, in effect, is nothing more than an application of Einstein's famous formula, $E = mc^2$, The Germans, Bothe and Becker, and the French physicists, Frédéric Joliot and Irène Joliot-Curie were studying the effects of alpha rays on thin metal foils when they noticed that the bombardment of a light metal, beryllium, with alpha particles produced a strange new form of radiation. Not until 1932

121 American physicist J. Robert Oppenheimer was in charge of the designing of the first atom bomb. Built at Los Alamos, it was set off on July 16, 1945, in New Mexico. Less than a month later, atom bombs were dropped on Hiroshima and Nagasaki, August 6 and 9, bringing on the end of World War II. The success of the atom bomb was also a tribute to the increased power of modern physics to penetrate and use the elemental forces of nature.

122 The "Baker Day" test explosion of an atomic bomb at Bikini Atoll, July 25, 1946 was carried out by the U.S. Army. By the end of the year all atomic activities of the United States had been placed under a civilian-controlled agency.

did James Chadwick demonstrate that this radiation consisted of neutral particles of a mass close to that of the proton. The neutron, predicted by Rutherford in 1920, had been discovered. The identification of the neutron was one of those events, almost unnoticed at the time, which was to have startling consequences, for it was to lead to nuclear energy and the atom bomb.

But now the era of the first atom-smashing machines had been reached. It was obvious that if a suitable projectile, or particle, could be found to produce nuclear disintegrations of practical value the knowledge of the atom's structure could be immeasurably advanced. To try to hit atomic nuclei with alpha particles, it was said, was like trying to shoot a rifle at the heads of pins scattered at random tens of yards apart. Protons would be fine projectiles, but how were they to be given the necessary speed? At the University of Princeton in 1931 Robert Van de Graaff had developed an electrostatic generator, the principle of which is very similar to that of the Wimshurst machine. The acceleration of the protons is produced with the aid of a high-voltage transformer at the bottom of the apparatus which feeds, via a metal comb, electric charges to a moving belt. The charge, carried to the top by the belt, is collected by another comb, thus creating between the top and the bottom a difference of potential which, from 80,000 volts in the first model, rose to 6,000,000 volts in the giant machine installed at Round Hill some years later.

Another type of accelerator was invented by Ernest O. Lawrence in 1930. The principle of the cyclotron is quite simple. At the center of the

123-131 The atom bomb is merely the most visible evidence of the striking advances in nuclear physics in recent years. Using atom smashers, reactors, radioactive materials and other new research tools, nuclear physicists have not only explored the core of the atom but have also made important contributions to industry, agriculture, medicine, electric power, and ship propulsion. Radioactive materials such as radioisotopes, for instance, are used extensively as tracers in the petroleum, metal, and textile industries, and in medicine and agriculture. A few special types of radioisotopes are produced in cyclotrons, such as the one shown here (123). Note the bending of light rays in the interior of this cyclotron under the influence of its strong magnetic field. But most radioisotopes are byproducts of nuclear fission in reactors, or are recovered from used fuel elements from the reactors. In working with such waste fuel elements, or irradiating certain materials or plants to produce chemical or genetic changes, operators must be shielded by concrete, metal, and glass, and must use remote-control devices as shown in the illustrations on this and subsequent pages (124, 125, 127) from the French atomic center at Saclay. These are sensitive enough to shave a man at a distance, if required. But the heart of the atomic industry is the reactor itself, such as the "Rubéole" critical assembly at Saclay, with its control rods (126) or the American research reactor, "Triga" (128, 129). Modern physics has also developed the laser (130), a ruby rod that produces a powerful beam of coherent light (here shown disintegrating a razor blade). It has many potential uses in communications, medicine, industry, power transmissions, and as a "death ray" weapon. Another device, the tiny semi-conductor, has revolutionized the capabilities of the computer. A digital hydraulics system shown here (131) will operate on computer command to control space vehicles.

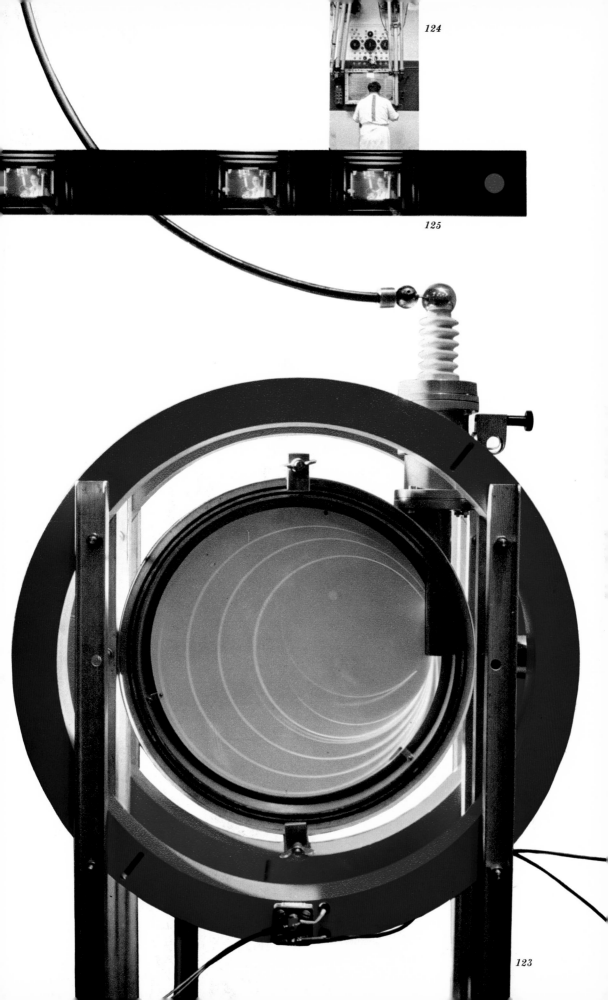

124

125

123

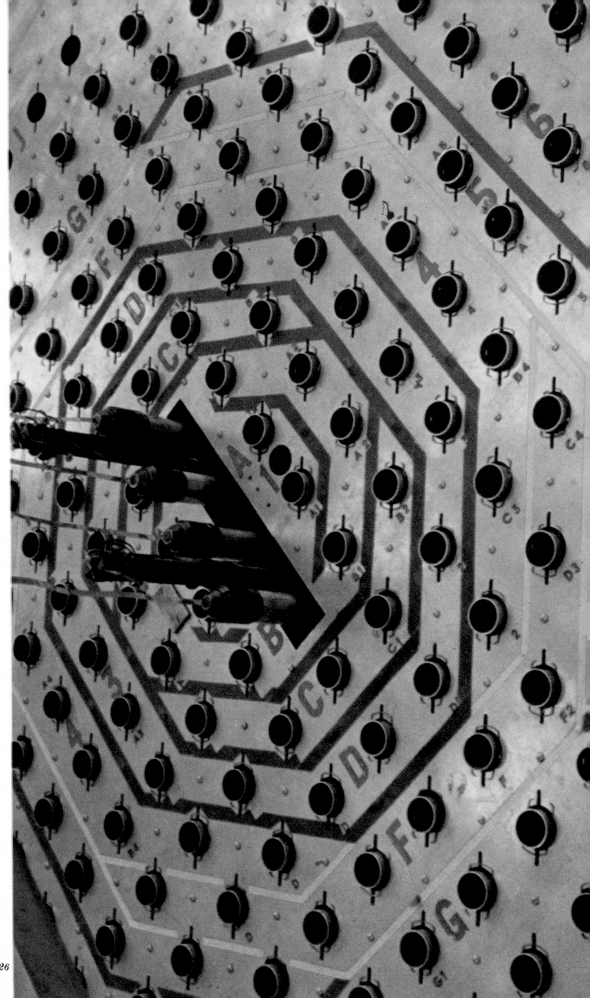

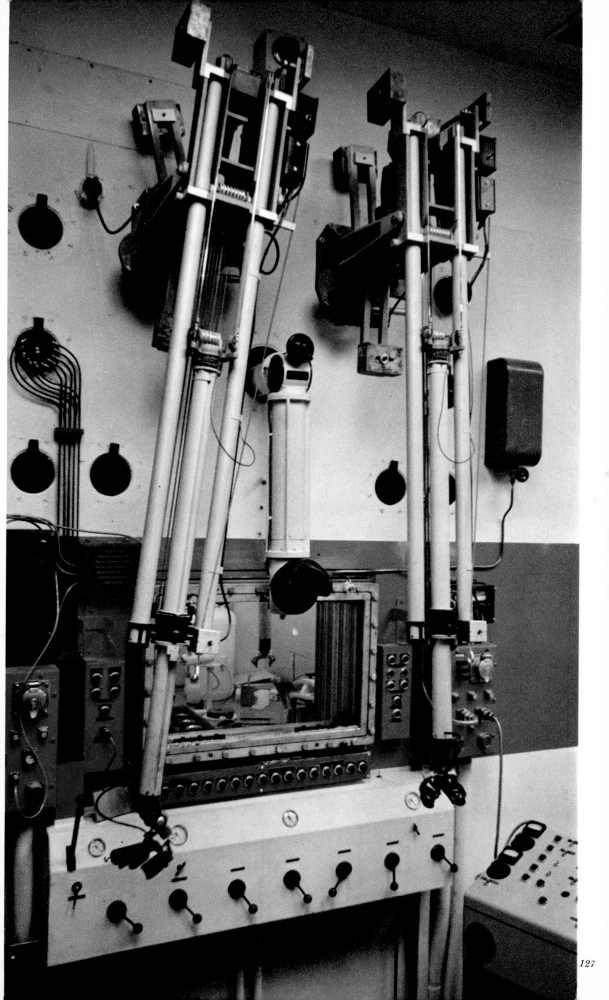

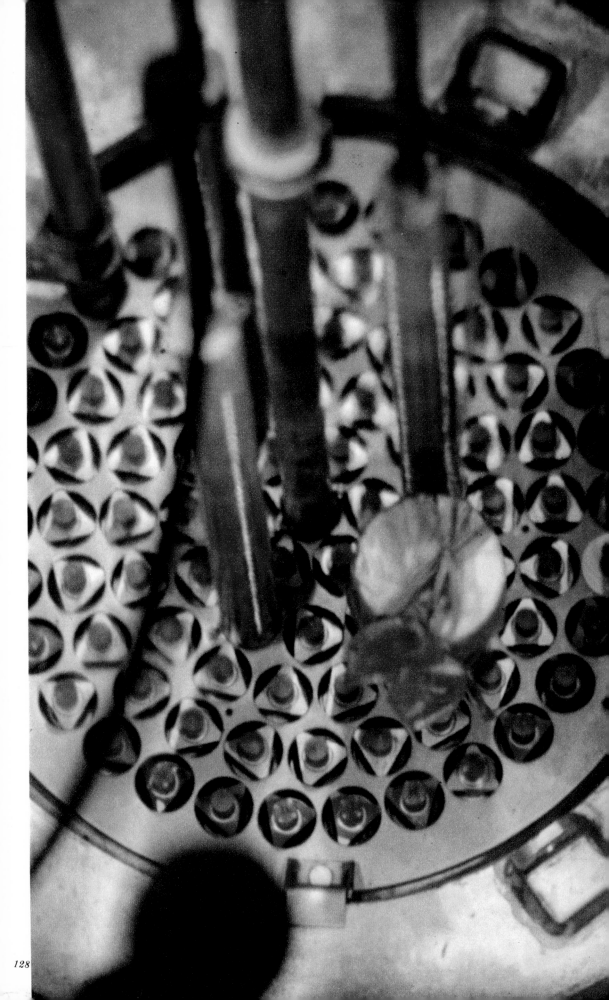

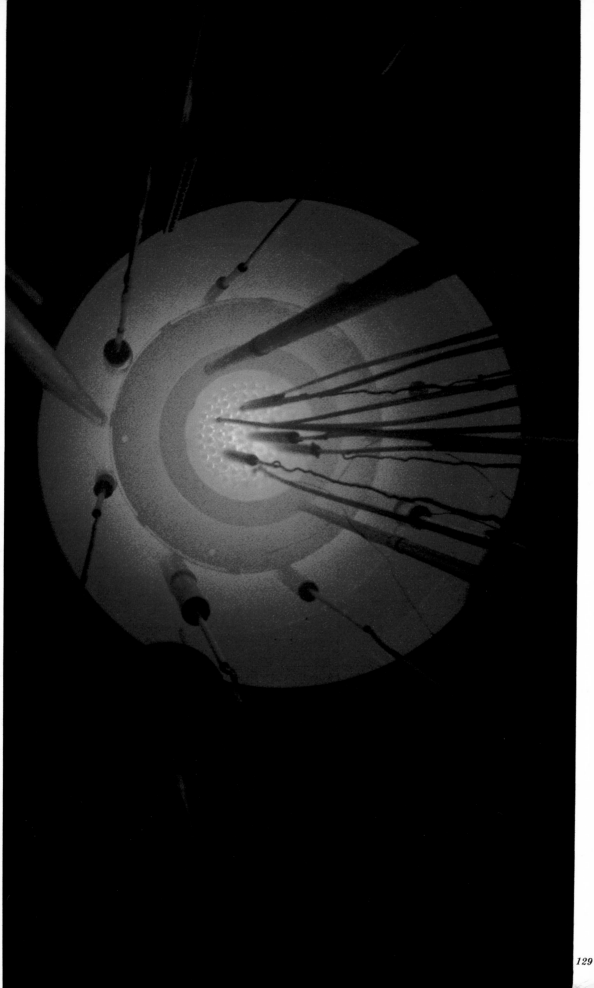

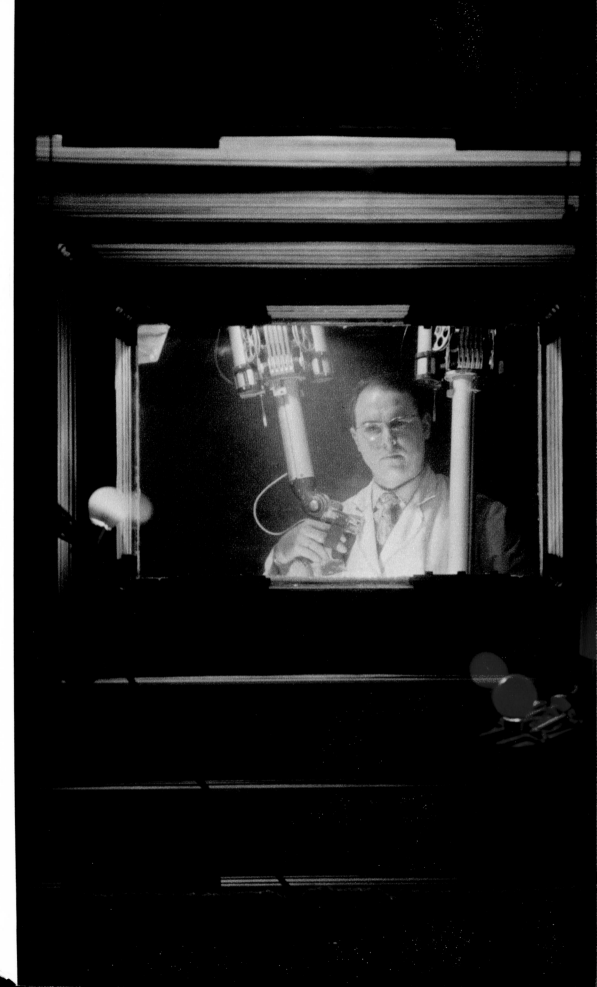

circular apparatus, in which the best possible vacuum has been created, atomic particles are injected at low energy. Subjected to an intense magnetic field created by a powerful electromagnet, the particles begin to turn in circles and are accelerated at each turn by an oscillating electric field between two D-shaped electrodes. As the particles accelerate they describe a spiral motion outwards towards the edge of the magnetic field, where they can be deflected against a target or extracted in the form of a beam. With modern cyclotrons it is possible to accelerate particles up to a considerable fraction of the velocity of light, giving them enough energy to disintegrate any atomic nucleus. But in order to examine the parts of the nucleus in detail, it was necessary to wait for the far more powerful synchrotron, invented just after the war. In a synchrotron the particles, accelerated by a pair of electrodes as in the cyclotron, travel on a circular orbit inside a narrow, doughnut-shaped vacuum vessel.

It is instructive to compare the modern giants with one of the pioneer "atom-smashers" built by John D. Cockcroft and E. T. S. Walton at Cambridge's Cavendish Laboratory in 1932. Using a transformer of only 150,000 volts they managed, with much ingenuity, to build up a difference in potential of 700,000 volts. With this they accelerated protons and were able to disintegrate lithium nuclei into two alpha particles. Thanks to the cloud chamber invented by C.T.R. Wilson between 1897 and 1912, the results of their labors were made clearly visible to the experimenters. (Wilson's wonderful apparatus not only shows up the trajectories of atomic particles in black and white as a chain of tiny water drops, but also enables them to be recorded in photographs. Cockcroft and Walton's photograph of their disintegration of lithium is reproduced in nearly all textbooks of physics, and even today this great historical record makes a profound impression.)

A "chain reaction," one nuclear disintegration setting off another, distinguishes the atom bomb and the nuclear reactor from the operations of the atom-smashers. The achievement of nuclear fission was preceded by a series of closely related discoveries concerned with the neutron. In 1934, for instance, Enrico Fermi discovered that neutrons slowed down in paraffin could produce nuclear disintegrations in a variety of atoms. Earlier in the same year the two Joliot-Curies had created a sensation at the staid Academy of the Sciences in Paris by announcing the discovery of artificial radioactivity. They had gradually come to the conclusion that it was possible to introduce extra neutrons into a nucleus and thus transform an innocuous piece of phosphorus, carbon, or cobalt into a radioactive form of the same substance. Thus the radioactive isotopes were discovered. Today they have become widely useful in medicine and industry.

But there was more to come. In 1939 the scientific world, already prepared for new developments in radioactivity, was set astir by the news that Otto Hahn, Lisa Meitner, Fritz Strassmann and Otto Frisch in Germany had discovered that the uranium nucleus, if suitably bombarded by neutrons, could be broken in two with the liberation of 100 million electron-volts of energy. In a report in the scientific review, *Nature*, Lisa Meitner explained that, like a drop

of water that has grown too big, the uranium nucleus, bombarded by neutrons, can no longer hold together, and bursts! Physicists around the world understood the implications.

Between this discovery and the explosion of the first atom bomb six years later many events, large and small, intervened. The anxious rivalry between the Allies and Germany was marked by the struggle to obtain supplies of heavy water, used as a moderator, to slow the chain reaction in early reactors. Early in 1940 the first minute amounts of the precious isotope, uranium 235 (used in the chain reaction) were separated from uranium 238 at the University of Minnesota. In the meantime the United States government had been brought into the project and in January, 1942, Enrico Fermi, Nobel prize-winner of 1938, moved his research team to Chicago where he built the first atomic "pile," or reactor. This began to operate for the first time on December 2, 1942, producing in the process two new elements, neptunium and plutonium, which McMillan, Seaborg, and Segre had already recognized in 1940 and 1941. From this point on the pace grew faster. The secret governmental Manhattan Project, set up to build a bomb, resulted in the first atom explosion on July 16, 1945 at Alamogordo, New Mexico, and finally the nuclear holocausts at Hiroshima and Nagasaki on August 6 and 9, 1945, which brought the war to a close.

The A-bomb was effective as a weapon; the H-bomb which followed, "kindling on earth the fire which drives the sun and stars," was (and is) altogether too effective. As early as 1934 the principle of the fusion of hydrogen into helium had been widely recognized as a probable source

133 *A Van de Graaff generator, capable of producing up to 600 kilowatts of direct current, at a Siemens research laboratory.*
134 *A high-voltage connection for CERN' model of an electrostatic separator.*

of stellar energy. A simple subtraction was enough to show that the reaction would give out enormous amounts of energy. In fact, the two nuclei of heavy hydrogen together add up to 4.02516 units of mass, while the nucleus of helium produced by their fusion weighs only 4.00390. Thus the disappearance of 0.02126 mass units of matter has to be accompanied by a corresponding liberation of energy in the order of 500,000 kw-h per gram-molecule of helium. This was considered by the scientists as an interesting reaction but of no practical importance, until in the 1950's development of the hydrogen bomb was started. Suddenly the world was terrified to learn that both the United States and Russia were testing thermonuclear devices, and finally bombs. In recent years this ominous testing has reached a crescendo of power; but there are signs that a more responsible attitude may be developing, particularly since other nations will soon have the H-bomb.

The hydrogen bomb at least served to put the scientists and engineers on the track of a new source of power, more economical than the older uranium reactors, wich are now springing up around the world like mushrooms, as well as providing power for submarines and icebreakers. The major difficulty in taming the thermonuclear reaction lies in creating a temperature on the order of several hundred million degrees, a feat which can be accomplished for a fraction of a second in the hydrogen bomb by means of a uranium trigger bomb, but which is still beyond the range of the ingenious, experimental British "Zeta" apparatus and the remarkable American "Stellarator." Nevertheless, experiments, magnetic and otherwise, in confining a

plasma which has already reached a temperature of two to three million degrees are being continued, although since 1958 progress has been disappointingly slow.

Returning to pure physics, we find that it was occupied in exploring the strange world of the atomic nucleus as well as the truly fantastic forms in which energy can be materialized. One of the most puzzling problems was how to explain the enormous forces which held the nucleus together in such a dense mass. Their nature did not seem to be electric. A clue came with the publication in 1935, by the Japanese physicist, Hideki Yukawa, of his hypothesis of the exchange of a new particle, called the meson, between the protons and neutrons of a nucleus. Yukawa showed that these particles should have a mass about 200 times that of the electron, and a very short "life-time," less than a millionth of a second. Later the mesons were separated into two types, the Pi-meson, responsible for the nuclear forces, and the Mu-meson. British studies of cosmic rays in photographic plates, undertaken in 1947, actually revealed the presence of Pi-mesons. During the following winter Pi-mesons were for the first time produced artificially in the giant synchrocyclotron at the University of California. Their trajectories were recognized on a photographic plate, with each one ending in a star, indicating that the meson had been absorbed by a nucleus which had then exploded.

The existence of anti-matter had been predicted by the English physicist Paul A. M. Dirac in 1929, in a note to the Royal Society. By 1935 the possibility of creating a proton-antiproton pair had been realized, but the energy

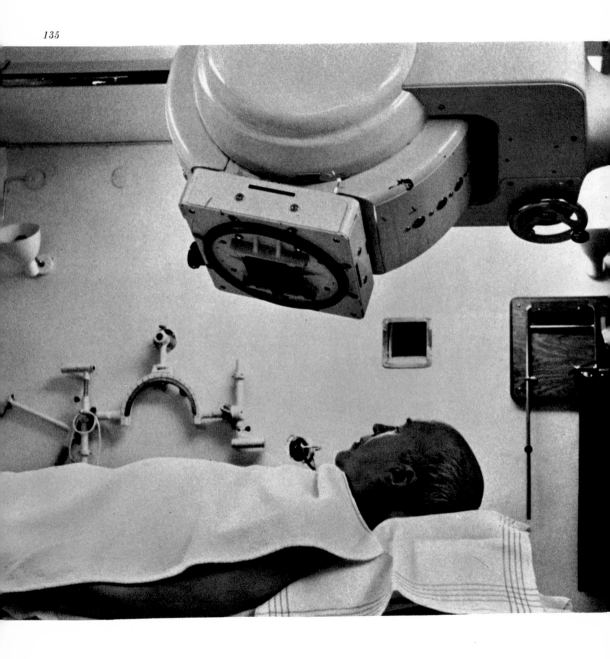

135   Radiation therapy is given to a
patient in Stockholm's Karolinska
Hospital. The use of radiation and
radioactive materials in medicine
has grown enormously in recent years.
Used as tracer elements, radioisotopes
are injected into the blood in tiny
doses to be followed with Geiger counters
or scintillometers. Radioactive iodine
is extensively used to diagnose
thyroid malfunctions, while
especially-designed research reactors
have proved effective with brain
tumors, cancer, and other disorders.
136   A lung cancer patient at
Teheran's Itan cancer research
institute is given radioactive cobalt
therapy. One of the most commonly
used radioisotopes, cobalt is less
expensive but as efficient as radium.

136

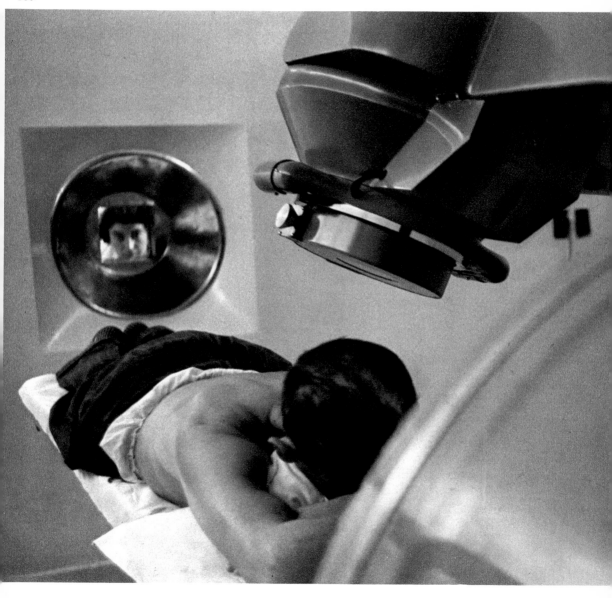

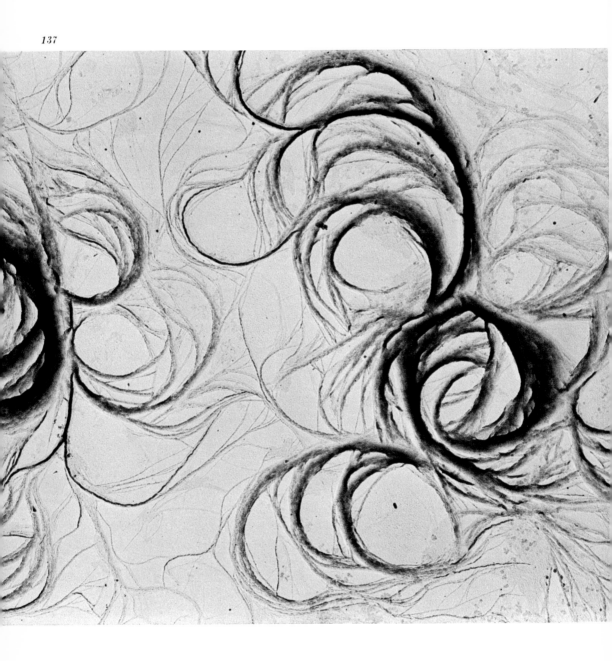

*137   Nylon, photographed through
an electron microscope at the
Battelle Memorial Institute in
Geneva and enlarged 20,000 times.
The electron microscope has a far
greater resolving power (ability to
produce clear images of objects
close together) than the ordinary
microscope. Instead of light, it
illuminates the object under
observation (prepared as a thin
film) with a beam of electrons
which carries an image forward to
be enlarged by an electrostatic or
magnetic focusing system. The
image is then received on a
fluorescent screen and photographed.
138   Photograph of gallium sulfide,
a rare compound, enlarged 80,000
times through an electron microscope.*

138

required was 6,000 million electric volts. This was finally achieved in the laboratory at Berkeley in 1955, and was soon followed by evidence for the existence of the antineutron. The corresponding particle for the electron, the positive electron, or positron, had already been discovered by Carl D. Anderson in cosmic rays in 1932. Later on, in 1937, the creation of electron pairs requiring only the relatively low energy output of about 1 million electron volts, was demonstrated. The neutrino and the antineutrino complete the series of leptons, or light particles. The neutrino, predicted 25 years before by the Swiss physicist W. Pauli, was not directly detected until it showed up in large scintillation counters installed at Savannah River in Georgia.

Further developments are awaited. In the meantime the physicists are working unceasingly to find out more about the internal structure of the atom. Powerful and expensive equipment has been brought into action, notably the two huge protonsynchrotrons at CERN (European Organization for Nuclear Research) near Geneva and at the Brookhaven National Laboratory near New York City, producing energies of around 30 billion electron volts each. According to the modern view, the study of high energy interactions involving different sorts of mesons may well provide the clue to the secrets of matter and anti-matter.

Where is physics going and what is its future? The great French scientist Leprince-Ringuet is not disposed to predict the future. "I can only tell you," he says, "that we are working, but without too much idea of what we shall be doing in the future; and that is, after all, what makes it so satisfying."

chronology

"Bottle-imp," a hydrostatic experiment, 1680

1230	Publication of Jordanus Nemorarius' work on gravity, "Gravitas Secundum Situs."
1249	Roger Bacon writes down a formula for gunpowder.
1269	Philosopher and engineer Peter Peregrinus describes a primitive compass.
1330	William of Heytesbury contradicts Aristotle's ideas about falling bodies, pointing out that a freely falling body goes three times as far in the second second of its fall as in the first.
1382	Nicole Oresme proposes his laws of ballistics.
1440	Nicolas de Cusa, studying hydraulics, invents the hygrometer (for measuring moisture) and the bathometer (for measuring depths in water).
1500	Approximate date of Leonardo da Vinci's work on hydrostatics, diffraction, capillarity, and flying machines.
1583	Galileo discovers the isochronism (regularity) of the pendulum.
1587	Galileo formulates his law of falling bodies ($h = \frac{1}{2} gt^2$).
1590	The mystic J. B. Porta publishes his "Natural Magic," which contains the first description of the camera obscura and the magnifying glass.
1604	Zacharias Jansen, reputedly copying an earlier Italian invention, builds a telescope.
1609	Invention of the Galilean, or astronomical telescope.
1611	Publication of Johannes Kepler's "Dioptrics" in which he describes the laws of refraction.
1612- 1620	Appearance of the first microscopes.
1620	Francis Bacon publishes his "Novum Organum" in which he emphasizes the experimental approach to the sciences.
1637	Publication of Descartes' "Dioptrics," which includes formulae for lenses.
1643	Torricelli's experiment demonstrates the existence of atmospheric pressure.
1648	Pascal's experiment on the Puy-de-Dôme confirms the correctness of Torricelli's conclusions.
1650	Otto von Guericke of Magdeburg invents the air pump with which he carries out his famous experiments with evacuated spheres.
1657	Foundation of the Florentine Accademia del Cimento, an institution for experimental research.

1660	Von Guericke invents the first machine to generate an electrical charge, by means of which he establishes the principle of electrical repulsion.
1662	The Royal Society is founded in London.
1662	Robert Boyle discovers the law which states that at a constant temperature the pressure of a gas multiplied by its volume is constant.
1666	Establishment of the Académie des Sciences at Paris.
1666	Isaac Newton formulates his theory of fluxions in his studies of calculus.
1668	Newton invents the reflecting, or mirror, telescope.
1672	Newton splits up white light with a prism and discovers the spectrum.
1675	The corpuscular theory of light is proposed by Newton.
1687	Publication of Newton's "Mathematical Principles of Natural Philosophy."
1690	Christiaan Huygens, in his "Essay on the Nature of Light," maintains that light is a wave motion in the aether, opposing Newton's corpuscular theory.
1690	Denis Papin proposes a steam piston, and may have built a model of it five years later.
1698	In England, Thomas Savery patents the first practical steam engine.
1701	Newton constructs a thermometer.
1702	Guillaume Amontons discovers that at a fixed pressure water always boils at the same temperature.
1707	Papin publishes his "New way of using the power of fire to raise water."
1712	Thomas Newcomen and John Calley build a steam engine for use in mines.
1714	Gabriel Daniel Fahrenheit invents his thermometer and measures the boiling points of several liquids.
1730	French physicist René-Antoine Réaumur devises a thermometer.
1733	Charles-François de Cisternay DuFay and the Abbé Nollet find that there are two kinds of electricity—"resinous," or negative, and "vitreous," or positive. They formulate the basic electrical law that "like charges repel and unlike charges attract."
1738	Nollet, a scientific popularizer, publishes his "Course in Experimental Physics."

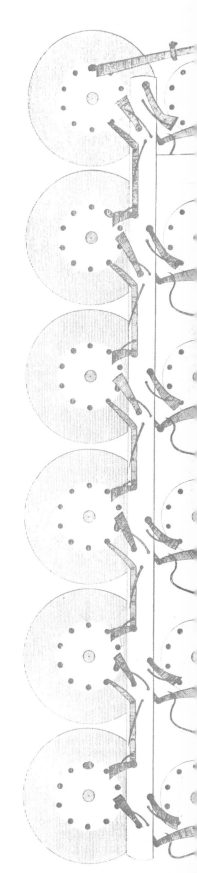

Insides of calculating machine, 18th century

1742 Anders Celsius applies a new scale to his thermometer.

1745 Pieter von Musschenbroek and E. G. von Kleist independently invent the Leyden jar, a device for storing and discharging electricity.

1787 Charles-Augustin de Coulomb establishes the basic laws of electrostatics and magnetism.

1796 Alessandro Volta invents the voltaic pile (the first real battery), a source of direct current electricity.

1801 Thomas Young discovers the phenomenon of interference in light.

1809 Gay-Lussac formulates his kinetic theory of gases.

1811 Amadeo Avogadro's hypothesis (that under the same conditions of temperature and pressure there is always the same number of molecules in a given volume of gas) is proposed and verified.

1818 Augustin Fresnel, studying diffraction and interference, formulates his wave theory of light.

1820 Hans Christian Oersted, Danish physicist, demonstrates that a current of electricity creates a magnetic field.

1821 English physicist Michael Faraday discovers that a charge on the outside of a closed conductor produces no electric field or force within the conductor.

1822 Physicists Arago and Villejuif carry out experiments in the speed of sound.

1823 Faraday liquifies several gases.

1824 Sadi Carnot, pioneer in thermodynamics, publishes his paper on "the motive power of fire."

1825 French Physicist André-Marie Ampère publishes a memoir explaining the nature of the electric current and its relation to magnetism.

1826 George Ohm formulates the law which states that in a given circuit, the current in amperes equals the pressure in volts divided by the resistance in ohms.

1831 Faraday, with the American, Joseph Henry, discovers the principle of electro-magnetic induction.

1833 Faraday discovers the laws of electro-chemical decomposition (electrolysis).

1847 James Prescott Joule establishes the mechanical equivalent of heat.

1849-1850 Léon Foucault and Hippolyte Fizeau measure the velocity of light.

1851 Foucault's pendulum demonstrates the rotation of the earth.

1854 Sinsteden invents an accumulator, or storage battery.

1859 Heinrich Helmholtz measures the vibration frequencies of musical notes.

1859 Julius Pflücker discovers cathode rays. The English scientist William Crookes, inventor of the famous Crookes tube, would later demonstrate that these rays have definite energy and momentum.

1861 Gustav Kirchhoff analyses the spectrum in terms of chemical bodies.

1865 James Clerk Maxwell publishes his electromagnetic theory of light.

1869 Zénobe Gramme invents the first practical dynamo.

1872 Gaston Planté constructs the first successful storage battery.

1879 Thomas Alva Edison invents his electric lamp, which revolutionizes the lighting of cities.

1884 Edison is given the first patent in the field of electronics, after having discovered the "Edison effect," basis of modern electronics.

1885-1892 Philipp von Lenard's experiments show that cathode rays carry a negative charge and can pass through metal foils.

1886 Eugen Goldstein discovers canal rays, streams of protons.

1887 Scientists Michelson and Morley carry out an experiment which disproves the existence of the aether.

1888 Heinrich Hertz, confirming Maxwell's electromagnetic theory, detects Hertzian, or radio waves in space.

1895 Jean Perrin obtains some evidence of the existence of the electron and puts forth his model of the atom.

1895 Wilhelm Roentgen discovers X-rays.

1896 Henri Becquerel discovers natural radioactivity.

1897 J. J. Thomson proposes his theory of the electron, based upon his study of the corpuscular nature of cathode rays.

1898 Discovery of radium by Pierre and Marie Curie.

1900 Max Planck revolutionizes physics with his theory of quanta, or discontinuous emission of energy.

1901 Guglielmo Marconi sends the first transatlantic wireless signal, from England to Newfoundland.

1903 F. Soddy and W. Ramsay show that radium disintegrates spontaneously with the emission of helium.

1905 Albert Einstein publishes his special theory of relativity and his theory of the photon, or "packet of light."

1907 Lee De Forest patents his three-electrode vacuum tube, the basis of electronics.

1907 Ernest Rutherford demonstrates that the alpha particle is a nucleus of ionized helium.

1910 Sir J. J. Thomson discovers isotopes.

1910 Robert A. Millikan calculates the charge and the mass of the electron.

1911 H. K. Onnes discovers super-conductivity in mercury.

1912 C. T. R. Wilson perfects his cloud chamber, which reveals tracks of individual atomic particles.

1913 Rutherford and Niels Bohr propose the "planetary system" models of the atom.

1913 William D. Coolidge produces a hot-cathode X-ray tube which operates at 100,000 volts.

1916 Arnold Sommerfeld modifies the Bohr theory of the atom, with elliptical orbits for the electrons.

1919 First artificial nuclear dis-integration: Rutherford trans-forms nitrogen into oxygen.

1920 Beginning of regular radio broadcasting, in the United States.

1920 Francis William Aston builds his mass spectroscope and begins to separate isotopes.

1923 American television pioneer, Charles Francis Jenkins, transmits pictures of President Harding from Washington to Philadelphia, 130 miles.

1925 Louis de Broglie publishes his theory of wave mechanics.

1926 Erwin Schroedinger, Werner Heisenberg, and Paul Dirac elaborate the theory of wave mechanics.

1926 Heisenberg publishes his studies of quantum mechanics, formulates his "Uncertainty Principle."

1928 Dirac predicts the existence of anti-particles.

1930 E. O. Lawrence invents the cyclotron which, accelerating atomic particles, gives them the necessary energy to disintegrate atomic nuclei.

Eratosthenes

Papin

Roentgen

Leucippus

Franklin

Hertz

Gassendi

Faraday

de Broglie

Francis Bacon

Volta

Irene Joliot-Curie

Torricelli

Kirchhoff

Thomson

Descartes

Antoine Becquerel

Fermi

Newton

Maxwell

Yang and
Lee

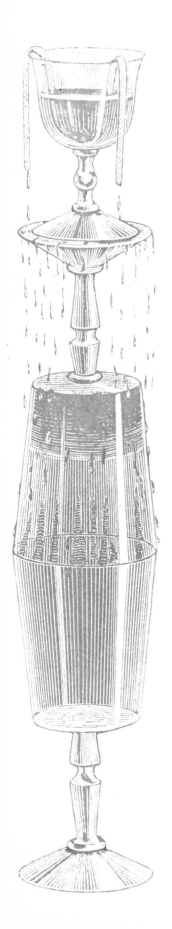

1931 Robert Van de Graaff develops his electrostatic generator for accelerating protons.

1931 Wolfgang Pauli of Austria predicts the existence of the particle which, in the following year, Enrico Fermi named the neutrino.

1932 Harold Urey discovers deuterium, an isotope of hydrogen, and heavy water.

1932 James Chadwick, in the United States, and Irene and Frederic Joliot-Curie, in France, discover the neutron.

1932 J. D. Cockcroft and E. T. S. Walton achieve the first nuclear fission, accelerating protons and disintegrating lithium into two alpha particles.

1932 Carl David Anderson discovers the positron, or anti-electron, in cosmic rays.

1934 Fermi uses neutrons slowed down in paraffin to produce nuclear reactions.

1934 Discovery of artificial radio-activity by the Joliot-Curies.

1935 Japanese physicist Hikeda Yakawa predicts the existence of the meson.

1936 Discovery of the Mu-meson or muon.

1938 Hans Bethe proposes his theory of stellar energy by nuclear fusion.

1938 P. Kapitza, J. F. Allen, and A. P. Misner discover the superfluidity of helium II, which is able to flow readily through narrow channels without apparent viscous resistance. In the same year, Tiza formulates his two-fluid theory, stating that the total density of a liquid may be divided into two parts.

1939 Discovery of uranium fission by Hahn, Meitner, Strassmann, and Frisch.

1940 First separation of uranium 235 from uranium 238, by Nifler.

1940 Glenn Seaborg identifies the new element, plutonium.

1941 Beginning of commercial television broadcasting, in the United States.

1942 First nuclear reactor, or "pile," constructed by Fermi in the United States.

1944 Leprince-Ringuet and L'Héritier discover the K-meson which has a mass between that of the pion and the proton.

1945 Experimental atomic bomb is exploded at Alamogordo, New Mexico, less than a month before the bombings of Hiroshima and Nagasaki.

1947 Cecil Frank Powell discovers the Pi-meson or pion.

1947 G. D. Rochester and C. D. Butler give the first evidence for the existence of hyperons, unstable particles whose mass exceeds that of neutrons.

1947-1948 First artificial production of pions in the Berkeley, California, synchrocyclotron.

1948 Invention of the transistor, widely used in electronics as a replacement for the vacuum tube.

1952 First thermonuclear (hydrogen) bomb is exploded at Bikini.

1955 The giant cyclotron at Berkeley shows up pairs of protons and anti-protons.

1956 Opening of the world's first atomic power station, generating electricity from nuclear power, at Calder Hall, England.

1956-1963 Plasma research aimed at the realization of power from nuclear fusion: the Stellarator in the United States, and Zeta in Great Britain.

1958 The neutrino, predicted 27 years before, is dectected at Savannah River, U.S.A.

1958 Physicists Lee and Yang suggest that the law of conservation of parity does not hold for weak interactions.

1958 C. H. Townes publishes an early work on masers (microwave amplification by stimulated emission of radiation).

1958 Publication of the phenomenon known as the Lamb-Rutherford Shift, based on studies by Rutherford and W. E. Lamb.

1961 Physicists at Berkeley and the University of California's Lawrence Radiation Laboratory discover the sub-atomic particle called the omega.

1961 The Brookhaven National Laboratory's huge alternating gradient synchrotron accelerates a beam of protons to an energy of 33 billion electron volts. This machine and the CERN proton synchrotron which went into service early in this year, are the two most powerful accelerators in the world.

1962 Discovery of the anti-xi-minus particle, announced simultaneously by researchers at CERN and at Brookhaven.

1962 An atomic reactor produces power for the American naval station at McMurdo, Antarctica.

*Among those who have assisted in the
preparation of this book grateful
acknowledgment must be made to
Courtlandt Canby, General Editor,
Helen Muller, Suzanne Patrick,
and Eric Tschumi of the ENI staff;
Professor Morris H. Shamos,
Chairman of the Department of Physics,
New York University,
who read the manuscript with care;
Marc Cramer, Conservateur,
Musée d'Histoire des Sciences, Geneva;
and CERN, Geneva.*

*Nicolas Bouvier and Roger-Jean Ségalat,
Picture Research.*

credits

*Battelle Memorial Institute, Geneva: 137,138
Bettmann Archive, New York: 114
Bibliothèque de Genève: 1-3, 7, 9, 10-15, 18,
20-23, 27, 33-40, 47, 48, 88, 90, 91, 104-107
Bibliothèque Nationale, Paris: 5, 8, 16, 17, 19,
24-26, 28-32, 41, 43-45, 46, 50-52,
54-60, 62, 64-66, 68-71, 76, 100, 103
Brown Brothers, New York: 122
CERN, Geneva: 121, 134
Collection Huguenin: 77-84
Collection Liebeskind: 85
Collection Palais de la Découverte, Paris: 112
Commissariat à l'Energie Atomique,
France: Photo Sudre 124-127, 132
Deutsches Museum, Munich: 49
Ecole de Médecine, Geneva: 72
Encyclopédie Panckoucke: 67
General Dynamics, New York: 128, 129
Giraudon, Paris: 6, 74
Harper's Monthly: 113
IBM, New York: 131
"La Science Amusante," Tom Tit, 1890: 4
"Le Monde Physique," Guillemin, 1886: 101
"L'Encyclopédie," Diderot, 1751: 61, 63
Len Sirman Press, Geneva: 117
"Les Mécaniques du Florentin Galilée,"
Le Père Mersenne, 1639: 42
Magnum, Paris: Photo Eric Lessing 123
Musée des Arts et Métiers, Paris: 86, 87,
92, 94, 96-99, 110, 111
Musée d'Histoire de l'Education, Paris: 102
Musée d'Histoire des Sciences, Geneva: 93,
95, 108, 109
Musée Pédagogique, Paris: 53
Rapho, Paris: Photo Rickard 116,
Photo Robert Doisneau 118, 120,
Photo Maurice Lamaud 139
RCA, New York: 130
Science Museum, London: 73, 75, 115
Siemens AG, Munich: 133
Société de lecture, Geneva: 89
University of Chicago: 119
World Health Organization, Geneva:
Photo Jean Mohr 135, Photo Philip Boucas 136*

Chronology

*Bibliothèque Nationale, Paris: 2-4, 6,
8, 9, 14, 16, 25
Brown Brothers, New York: 18
CERN, Geneva: 23
Collection Erik Nitsche: 22
Collection George Sirot: 15
Culver, New York: 12, 13, 17, 21
Editions Bordas: 7
Giraudon, Paris: 5
"La Science Amusante," Tom Tit, 1890: 24
Musée Pédagogique, Paris: 11, 19, 20
"Physiologia Kircheriana," 1660, Bibliothèque
de Genève: 1
Science Museum, London: 10*

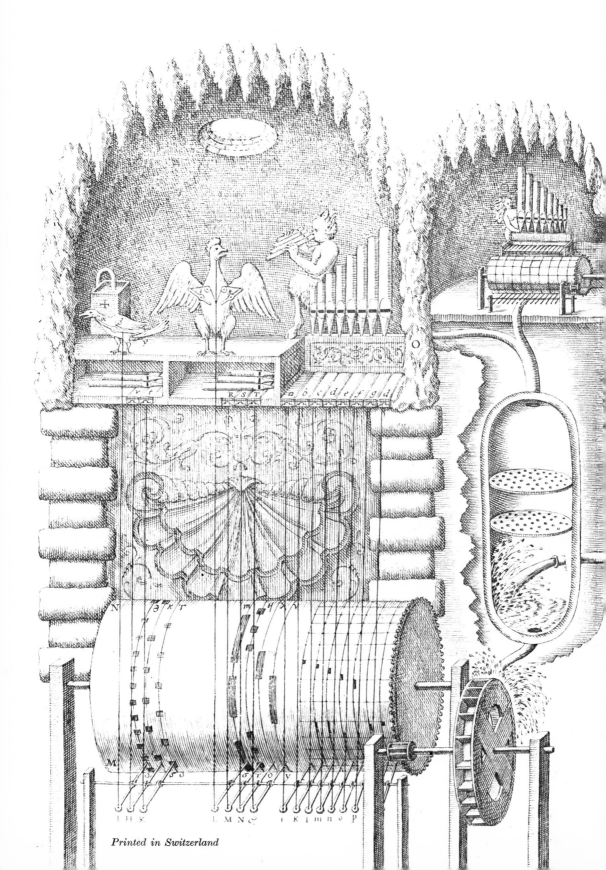